Contents

HSE
Health & Safety
Executive

A guide to the Radiation (Emergency Preparedness and Public Information) Regulations 2001

GUIDANCE ON REGULATIONS

L126

HSE BOOKS

This guidance is issued by the Health and Safety Executive. Following the
guidance is not compulsory and you are free to take other action. But if you
do follow the guidance you will normally be doing enough to comply with the
law. Health and safety inspectors seek to secure compliance with the law and
may refer to this guidance as illustrating good practice.

The Radiation (Emergency Preparedness and Public Information) Regulations 2001 (REPPIR) (made under the Health and Safety at Work etc Act 1974[1] (the 1974 Act), except regulation 17 which is made under the European Communities Act 1972) implement the articles on intervention in cases of radiation (radiological) emergency in Council Directive 96/29/Euratom[2] in Great Britain. The Directive lays down the basic safety standards for the protection of the health of workers and the general public against the dangers arising from ionising radiation (the BSS96 Directive).

REPPIR replace regulation 26 (special hazard assessments) and associated provisions of the Ionising Radiations Regulations 1985 (the 1985 Regulations) for premises and transport operations, ie REPPIR revoke these provisions, which were 'saved' by the Ionising Radiations Regulations 1999[3] (the 1999 Regulations). Transport operations in REPPIR mean rail transport and transferring or conveying through any public place other than by rail, road, inland waterway, sea or air or by means of a pipeline or similar means (ie standard transport modes or pipelines).

The 1999 Regulations, which implement most of the BSS96 Directive, replaced the 1985 Regulations which implemented most of the earlier 1980 Directive 80/836/Euratom (as amended by 84/467/Euratom). Where requirements of REPPIR overlay those of the 1999 Regulations, consistent drafting has been applied, for example regulation 4 of REPPIR and regulation 7 of the 1999 Regulations. There are some direct links between REPPIR and the 1999 Regulations, for example regulation 14 of REPPIR on emergency exposures, and regulations 21 and 24 of the 1999 Regulations on dose assessment, dose recording and medical surveillance. Different sectors use different terms to express a particular issue. The terminology used in REPPIR is as closely aligned as possible to that in the 1999 Regulations.

REPPIR apply to premises and transport operations. If radioactive substances are handled and stored, even temporarily, at ports and airports, the places where they are stored are regarded as premises and REPPIR will apply if sufficient quantities are involved. Emergency preparedness for the transport of radioactive substances by road, air, sea and inland waterway will be covered by the relevant modal transport legislation, to be updated by the Department for Transport, Local Government and the Regions (DTLR). NB All aspects of Articles 48 to 52 of the BSS96 Directive for road, air and sea/inland waterways will be implemented and enforced, where appropriate, through DTLR modal legislation by the Radioactive Materials Transport Division (RMTD), Civil Aviation Authority (CAA) and Maritime and Coastguard Agency (MCA), respectively. Until then, REPPIR include savings (ie regulation 26 and associated provisions) for these transport modes from the 1985 Regulations. These savings will be revoked in due course.

The Public Information for Radiation Emergencies Regulations 1992[4] (PIRER) implemented the Council Directive 89/618/Euratom[5] on informing the general public about health protection measures to be applied and steps to be taken in the event of a radiation (radiological) emergency. REPPIR partly subsume PIRER (ie regulation 3 for premises and transport operations and regulation 4). Until DTLR modal legislation is amended, REPPIR include savings (ie regulation 3 of PIRER) for these transport modes. These savings will be revoked in due course.

REPPIR regulation 17 (Duty of local authority to supply information to the public in the event of a radiation emergency) is made under the European Communities Act 1972 and is applicable to ALL local authorities, irrespective of the rest of REPPIR.

Northern Ireland and Gibraltar are producing their own regulations.

Consistency with other regulations

Emergency preparedness for accidents which may affect members of the public involves many external organisations, such as local authorities and emergency services. It is beneficial to such external organisations if legislative requirements for emergency preparedness which affect them are similar for different industries. Also, some companies are active in more than one of these major hazards sectors. The proposals for REPPIR have been developed alongside proposals for two other pieces of legislation: the Control of Major Hazards Regulations 1999[6] (COMAH) (to implement Council Directive 96/82/EC on the control of major accident hazards involving dangerous substances, known as the Seveso II Directive), and the amendment to the Pipelines Safety Regulations 1996[7] (still under development). This approach will achieve the aim of maximising consistency on emergency preparedness between Regulations for major hazards sectors, including the nuclear, chemicals and pipelines industries. The proposals have also been developed alongside existing rail legislation, and in particular the Packaging, Labelling and Carriage of Radioactive Materials by Rail Regulations 1996[8] (the 1996 Regulations), as amended by SI 1999/303, The Carriage of Dangerous Goods (Amendment) Regulations, and the Railway Safety Case Regulations 2000[9] (RSCR). Areas of overlap between REPPIR and these rail regulations are indicated in this guidance document.

The BSS96 Directive gives aims to be achieved in emergency preparedness, but does not include administrative details, such as timescales, to give effect to those aims. REPPIR therefore use the administrative arrangements for emergency planning in COMAH (regulations 9 to 13) which are largely taken from the Seveso II Directive (Article 11). Where no relevant administrative arrangements are given in COMAH, those in the 1999 Regulations and PIRER are used as tried and tested administrative arrangements.

Introduction

1   The main aim of REPPIR and the supporting guidance is to:

(a)   establish a framework for the protection of the public through emergency preparedness for radiation accidents with the potential to affect members of the public, from premises and specified transport operations; and

(b)   ensure the provision of information to the public:

    (i)   in advance in situations where a (REPPIR) radiation emergency might arise; and

    (ii)   in the event of any kind of radiation emergency (however it may arise).

Interface with the Nuclear Installations Act 1965[10] (NIA65)

2   REPPIR does not replace the existing nuclear site licence conditions, but for operators of nuclear licensed sites, compliance with these conditions should satisfy equivalent provisions in REPPIR.

3   All operators need arrangements in place to demonstrate their compliance with REPPIR to the Health and Safety Executive (HSE) (as the regulator).

Application/Scope of the Regulations

4   REPPIR apply to work with ionising radiation which may have the capability of producing a radiation emergency as defined. The requirements for application are in regulation 3. Exemptions are provided where work with ionising radiation would not lead to a reasonably foreseeable radiation emergency, such as work with non-dispersible sources or Type B packages. REPPIR apply to premises (including nuclear sites) and transport operations (ie rail transport and transferring or conveying through any public place other than by rail, road, inland waterway, sea or air or by means of a pipeline or similar means (ie standard transport modes or pipelines)).

5   One key aspect of REPPIR is that they place duties on 'carriers' of radioactive substances. These will generally be train operators in the sense used in the 1996 Regulations. However, carriers can choose either to carry out relevant duties themselves or to 'ensure that the duty is carried out' by someone else. This will in most cases be the consignor.

Responsibility for emergency planning

6   The operator's (on-site) emergency plan is the responsibility of the operator, the carrier's transport emergency plan is the responsibility of the carrier and the off-site emergency plan (for premises) is the responsibility of the local authority. Each has the duty to ensure that plans are prepared and are adequate and fit for purpose. In all cases the exchange of information between the duty holders and all the other organisations with an interest is central to the planning process and there will need to be extensive consultation with all these parties.

7   All these organisations with a role in responding to a reasonably foreseeable radiation emergency must be involved, as appropriate, in the preparation of emergency plans. Many of their interests will overlap and may, on occasion, conflict. Co-operation is essential (see guidance on regulation 11) and compromise may sometimes be necessary. Nominated representatives of

the principal organisations which could have a role to play in a radiation emergency should meet as an emergency co-ordinating group, or other similar group, to develop plans and testing regimes, and consult other organisations.

Purpose of emergency plans

8   An emergency plan is a document that explains the principles by which a reasonably foreseeable radiation emergency will be handled. It describes roles and responsibilities and may be supplemented by other detailed documentation. It can also provide the basis for dealing with radiation emergencies that are not reasonably foreseeable through the concept of extendibility (see paragraph 138 in the 'Emergency plans' section).

9   The emergency plan should address the response required during all the phases of the emergency, both the immediate needs and longer term recovery. The first few hours after the accident occurs is the 'critical' phase of an accident response, when key decisions, which will greatly affect the success of any mitigation measures, must be made within a short period of time and when those responsible will be under considerable pressure. Therefore, a detailed understanding of the likely sequence of events and appropriate countermeasures is of great benefit for all those who may reasonably be expected to have a role to play.

10   Current UK arrangements for integrated emergency management and response are contained in the Home Office* publication *Dealing with disaster*[11] and its Scottish equivalent *Dealing with disasters together.*[12]

Beginning of a radiation emergency

11   A radiation emergency begins when an emergency plan is implemented to deal with an event which leads to (or is likely to lead to) a member of the public receiving a dose of ionising radiation above the levels specified in Schedule 1.

12   There is a need to identify when a radiation emergency begins because of authorising emergency exposures. This reflects that an emergency plan may be implemented before the event has escalated to the point where members of the public receive the stated doses. By implementing the emergency plan, it usually should be possible to avert the worst outcome.

13   In the nuclear industry, a 'site incident' would usually be declared when a radiation emergency begins; whether or not a 'nuclear emergency' would be declared would depend upon the circumstances.

Emergency exposures

14   REPPIR make provision for emergency exposures in the event of a radiation emergency. These are exposures which exceed normal dose limits and are incurred by intervention personnel, who take action to bring help to endangered people, prevent exposure of a large number of people, or save valuable plant or goods. They are only permitted for authorised personnel who have received appropriate information and training and are appropriately equipped. The exposure of such people must be controlled so that the doses they receive are kept within predetermined dose levels.

---

* *Ministerial responsibility for emergency planning has moved from the Home Office to the Cabinet Office.*

Radiation protection and emergency planning specialists

15   Within REPPIR, advice should be sought from relevant radiation protection and emergency planning specialists wherever necessary.

Consultation with employees

16   There are legal requirements to consult with employees on health and safety issues in the Safety Representatives and Safety Committees Regulations 1977[13] (SI 1977/500, as amended by the Management of Health and Safety at Work Regulations SI 1992/5051 (as amended by SI 1999/3242) and Police (Health and Safety) Regulations SI 1999/860) and the Health and Safety (Consultation with Employees) Regulations 1996 (SI 1996/1513).[14] REPPIR include a requirement to consult employees about operators' emergency plans (regulation 7).

NEPLG

17   The Department of Trade and Industry (DTI) has a lead department role in bringing together organisations involved in off-site nuclear emergency planning through the Nuclear Emergency Planning Liaison Group (NEPLG). Members include representatives of the nuclear operators, police, fire service, local authority emergency planning officers and Government departments and agencies which would be involved in the response to an emergency. NEPLG provides a forum for discussing common problems, exchanging information and experience and agreeing improvements in planning, procedures and organisation. NEPLG has issued a consolidated guidance document[15] (also available on the DTI website) aimed at all those involved in the development of site-specific emergency plans at local level. NEPLG also reviews results of Level 2 and 3 emergency exercises carried out under Licence Condition 11 (NIA65), to ensure that important lessons learned from those exercises are put into practice. The role of NEPLG is explained in Chapter 7 of the HSE publication *Arrangements for responding to nuclear emergencies*.[16]

Citation and commencement

These Regulations may be cited as the Radiation (Emergency Preparedness and Public Information) Regulations 2001 and shall come into force on 20th September 2001.

Interpretation

(1)   In these Regulations, unless the context otherwise requires -

"the 1996 Regulations" means the Packaging, Labelling and Carriage of Radioactive Material by Rail Regulations 1996;(a)

(a) SI 1996/2090, amended by SI 1999/303.

18   These Regulations provide definitions of low specific activity (LSA), surface contaminated objects (SCO), special form radioactive material, Type B packages and special arrangement transport operations for Type B packages. These Regulations are referred to as the 1996 Regulations.

"the 1999 Regulations" means the Ionising Radiations Regulations 1999;(b)

"the Agency" in relation to premises or transport or a plan relating to premises or transport -

(a)   in England and Wales, means the Environment Agency,

(b)   in Scotland, means the Scottish Environment Protection Agency;

"approved dosimetry service" means an approved dosimetry service within the meaning of the 1999 Regulations and which is approved for the purpose of regulation 14 of these Regulations;

"carrier" shall be construed in accordance with paragraph (2);

"carrier's emergency plan" shall be construed in accordance with regulation 8;

"consignor" means an employer carrying out work with ionising radiation who presents to a carrier for transport by rail a consignment of any radioactive substance;

"dose assessment" means the dose assessment made and recorded by an approved dosimetry service in accordance with regulation 21 of the 1999 Regulations;

"dose record" means the record made and maintained in respect of an employee by the approved dosimetry service in accordance with regulation 21 of the 1999 Regulations;

"emergency exposure" means an exposure of an employee engaged in an activity of or associated with the response to a radiation emergency or potential radiation emergency in order to bring help to endangered persons, prevent exposure of a large number of persons or save a valuable installation or goods, whereby one of the individual dose limits referred to in paragraphs 1 or 2 of Part I of Schedule 4 to the 1999 Regulations could be exceeded;

(b) SI 1999/3232.

19   The dose limits in the 1999 Regulations, Schedule 4, Part 1, paragraphs 1 and 2, are for employees of 18 years of age or above.

"emergency services" means -

(a)   those police, fire and ambulance services who are likely to be required to respond to a radiation emergency which has occurred at the premises of an operator or at the location of a radiation emergency during the course of the transport of a radioactive substance, and

(b)   where appropriate, Her Majesty's Coastguard;

"the Executive" means the Health and Safety Executive;

"health authority" means, in relation to England and Wales, a health authority established under section 8 of the National Health Service Act 1977[(a)] and, in relation to Scotland, a health board established under section 2 of the National Health Service (Scotland) Act 1978;[(b)]

"installation" means a unit in which the radioactive substances present are, or are intended to be, produced, used, handled or stored, and it includes -

(a)   equipment, structures, pipework, machinery and tools,

(b)   railway sidings, docks and unloading quays serving the unit, and

(c)   jetties, warehouses or similar structures, whether floating or not, which are necessary for the operation of the unit;

(a) 1977 c.49; section 8 was substituted by the Health Authorities Act 1995 (c.17), section 1(1).
(b) 1978 c.29; section 2 was amended by the Health and Social Services and Social Security Adjustments Act 1983 (c. 41), Schedule 7.

20   Premises (see guidance on premises in paragraphs 36-45) constitute one or more installations, such as buildings or facilities where radioactive substances are produced, used, handled or stored. Such buildings or facilities may be served by, for example, railway sidings at nuclear licensed sites, or jetties/quays at ports, and such railway sidings or jetties/quays are considered as part of those particular installations. Container parks at ports would also count as installations or premises in their own right.

"intervention" means a human activity that prevents or decreases the exposure of persons to radiation from a radiation emergency or from an event which could lead to a radiation emergency, by acting on the sources of radiation, the paths by which such radiation may be transmitted to persons and on persons themselves;

"ionising radiation" means the transfer of energy in the form of particles or electromagnetic waves of a wavelength of 100 nanometres or less or a frequency of 3×10^{15} hertz or more capable of producing ions directly or indirectly;

"licensed site" means a site in respect of which a nuclear site licence has been granted and is in force;

21   A nuclear site licence is granted under NIA65.

"licensee" means the person to whom a nuclear site licence has been granted;

"local authority" means -

(a)   subject to sub-paragraphs (b) and (c) below, in relation to -

(i)   London, the London Fire and Emergency Planning Authority,

(ii)   an area where there is a fire and civil defence authority, that authority,

(iii) the Isles of Scilly, the Council of the Isles of Scilly,

(iv)   an area in the rest of England, the county council for that area or, where there is no county council for that area, the district council for that area,

(v)   an area in Scotland, the council for the local government area, and

(vi)   an area in Wales, the county council or the county borough council for that area;

(b) for the purposes of regulation 16(2), in relation to -

(i)   London, the London Fire and Emergency Planning Authority, and, in the City of London, the Common Council for the City of London, or, in an area in the rest of London, the London Borough Council for that area,

(ii)   any other area where there is a fire and civil defence authority, that authority and the district council for that area,

(iii) the Isles of Scilly, the Council of the Isles of Scilly,

(iv)   an area in the rest of England, the county council, if any, for that area and the district council, if any, for that area,

(v)   an area in Scotland, the council for the local government area, and

(vi)   an area in Wales, the county council or the county borough council for that area;

(c) for the purposes of regulation 16(3), in relation to -

(i)   the City of London, the Common Council for the City of London,

(ii)   an area in the rest of London, the London Borough Council for that area,

(iii) the Isles of Scilly, the Council of the Isles of Scilly,

(iv)   an area in the rest of England, the district council for that area or, where there is no district council for that area, the county council for that area,

(v)   an area in Scotland, the council for the local government area, and

(vi)   an area in Wales, the county council or the county borough council for that area;

2(1)

22   Local authorities have duties in connection with the preparation, review, revision, testing and implementation of off-site emergency plans (regulations 9, 10 and 13) and in making arrangements to supply information in the event of a radiation emergency (regulation 17). They may also be involved in the dissemination of operators' and rail carriers' prior information to the public (regulation 16(3)). If there are two levels of local authority in an area, then both levels have a function under regulation 16(2). This definition of 'local

2(1)

authority' identifies which authority has the above responsibilities in any given part of Great Britain. (Local authorities also have duties other than those described here under REPPIR.)

23   Within the Isles of Scilly, the local authority for all purposes in REPPIR is the Council of the Isles of Scilly; in Scotland, it is the council for the local government area; and in Wales it is the county council or county borough council for the area.

24   In London, the duty holder for off-site emergency plans and for making arrangements to supply information is the London Fire and Emergency Planning Authority. The local authority for dissemination of prior information is the Common Council for the City of London and the London Borough Councils.

25   In the rest of England:

(a)   in areas where there is a fire and civil defence authority, the duty holder for off-site emergency plans and for making arrangements to supply information is the fire and civil defence authority. The local authority for dissemination of prior information is the metropolitan district council;

(b)   in areas where there is both a county council and district council, the duty holder for off-site emergency plans and for making arrangements to supply information is the county council, and the local authority for dissemination of prior information is the district council;

(c)   in areas where there is a county council operating without a district council (known as a unitary authority), that council is the local authority for all purposes in REPPIR;

(d)   in areas where there is a district council operating without a county council and there is no fire and civil defence authority (known as a unitary authority), that council is the local authority for all purposes in REPPIR.

"medical surveillance" means medical surveillance carried out in accordance with regulation 24 of the 1999 Regulations;

"member of the public" means any person not being -

(a)   a person for the time being present upon premises where a radiation emergency is reasonably foreseeable or where a radiation emergency has actually occurred, or

(b)   a person engaged in an activity of or associated with the response to a radiation emergency;

26   The term 'member of the public' is used in the definition of 'radiation emergency' to identify those people who may have an entitlement to receive information under regulation 16 (Prior information to the public) and regulation 17 (Duty of local authority to supply information to the public in the event of a radiation emergency). The term should be interpreted as covering everyone except those who fall into the two excluded groups, that is everyone on-site or intervention personnel (see paragraph 28).

27   The first excluded group (everyone on-site) covers employees on the premises, including those of contractors, and other visitors who are on premises where a radiation emergency is reasonably foreseeable or has actually

occurred. This includes patients attending or people visiting hospitals, and students attending educational or research establishments. Their information needs should be catered for by the operator's emergency plan.

28   The second excluded group (intervention personnel) covers those engaged in or associated with the emergency response, on- or off-site. Such people may not have anticipated exposure to radiation from the emergency except for the fact that their organisation has a role to play in the emergency response and they have therefore been brought into the vicinity of the emergency. Such organisations would include the emergency services, but also, depending on the circumstances, could include Government departments and agencies, local authorities and health authorities/boards.

29   A radiation emergency could arise at a large site with a number of employers working in separate but nearby premises. The transit storage arrangements at ports and airports, such as warehouses are an example. One or more employers could be undertaking work with ionising radiation. Each individual employer who holds quantities of radioactive substances above the REPPIR thresholds in separate premises will be an operator under REPPIR. In such cases, people at the other premises (including other REPPIR premises) are members of the public for the purposes of REPPIR (except intervention personnel). The information needs of all such people are catered for by their employers under regulation 9(14).

30   Similarly, there may be two adjacent premises to which REPPIR applies, for example two nuclear licensed sites under the control of two separate operators at a large site. In such cases, the employees and other people on the adjacent premises should be considered as members of the public for emergency planning purposes (except employees on the adjacent site acting as intervention personnel), even though the emergency arrangements for both nuclear licensed sites are likely to be integrated.

31   There may also be two adjacent premises to which REPPIR applies where access by external agencies to one of the premises may be restricted or denied (for example Ministry of Defence (MoD) controlled premises). This should be established at the time that emergency plans are being prepared, and suitable arrangements should be drawn up and agreed at a local level to meet local needs to minimise doses to non-intervention employees on the adjacent site. REPPIR provides the framework for such discussions and arrangements under regulation 11 on consultation and co-operation.

2(1)

"non-dispersible source" means a sealed source or a radioactive substance which in either case by virtue of its physical and chemical form cannot cause a radiation emergency in any reasonably foreseeable event but it does not include any radioactive substance inside a nuclear reactor or any nuclear fuel element;

32   Operators (but not carriers) who work solely with radioactive substances that have physical and chemical properties that render them incapable of significant dispersal to atmosphere, water courses or sewers during any reasonably foreseeable event such as a fire or explosion, have no duties under these Regulations. 'Significant' in this context relates to whether such dispersal is capable of causing a radiation emergency and, in this regard, radiation dose to members of the public in the year following the emergency is the relevant issue (Schedule 1).

33   Operators who consider that all the radioactive substances they work with satisfy the requirements of non-dispersibility must complete an assessment to confirm this conclusion; this is a general requirement of the Management of Health and Safety at Work Regulations 1999[17] (MHSWR). In

2(1)

particular, HSE expects operators to be able to confirm that it is the robustness and/or chemical inertness of the radioactive substances they use that make them non-dispersible rather than the low public exposure risk that results from a 'dispersive' event such as a fire, although this is a relevant factor.

34   As a general rule, only solid, non-combustible radioactive substances or radioactive substances that are encapsulated in solid, non-combustible materials should be considered worth assessing for their non-dispersibility. When completing such assessments, operators should consider the matters set out in Figures 1 and 2 in Appendix 1.

35   If the radioactive substances an operator uses are each fully compliant with a relevant sealed source performance standard, to the extent that each can adequately withstand temperatures of at least 800°C and external pressures in excess of 7 MPa, the operator may consider them to be non-dispersible provided that their recommended working lives, as specified by their manufacturer(s), have not been exceeded. In such cases, completion of a full dispersibility assessment for each radioactive substance will not be necessary.

"nuclear site licence" has the meaning assigned to it by section 1(1) of the Nuclear Installations Act 1965;[(a)]

"off-site emergency plan" shall be construed in accordance with regulation 9;

"operator" shall be construed in accordance with paragraph (3);

"operator's emergency plan" shall be construed in accordance with regulation 7;

"premises" means -

(a)   the whole area under the control of the same person where radioactive substances are present in one or more installations, and for this purpose two or more areas under the control of the same person and separated only by a road, railway or inland waterway shall be treated as one whole area, or

(b)   where radioactive substances are present on a licensed site, that licensed site,

and, where a radioactive substance forms an integral part of a vessel and is used in connection with the operation of that vessel, it includes that vessel when it is at fixed point moorings or alongside berths, save that such vessel shall be deemed to be separate premises only where such moorings or berths do not form part of a licensed site or part of premises under the control of the Secretary of State for Defence;

(a) 1965 c.57; section 1 was amended by SI 1974/2056 and SI 1990/1918.

Hospitals and universities

36   Hospital and university campuses are single premises. Separate facilities in which work with ionising radiation is undertaken on such campuses under the overall control of the hospital or university administration, such as independently-funded research units, are installations within those premises. Only separate facilities that are physically located on the campus but are completely outside the control of the hospital or university administration, such as a completely independent science park with its own separate administration, should be considered as separate premises.

10

37   Individual hospital or university buildings that are not located on a campus are separate premises, except where two or more buildings are co-located (separated only by a right of way such as a road), where such co-located buildings would together form a single premises.

Industrial complexes

38   An industrial complex under the control of one person is a single premises, and would cover all facilities run by all employers on the complex. Only facilities which are on the industrial complex but which are completely outside the control of the industrial complex administration should be considered as separate premises.

Ports and airports

39   At ports and airports, all co-located areas within the port or airport (separated only by, for example, a road or railway) under the control of the same person together form one premises. A particular person may, therefore, have more than one premises within a port or airport if the areas under the control of that person are remote from one another (eg transit sheds).

40   Once REPPIR quantities (see Schedule 2) of radioactive substances have been unloaded from a ship or aircraft onto the quayside or tarmac they should be treated as part of the premises and the person in control of the premises (usually on which they are handled and stored) is responsible for any relevant REPPIR assessments and emergency plans. Therefore, the interface between transport and premises is the point at which they have been unloaded, or loading begins (see paragraph 64 on definition of 'transport').

41   When the radioactive substances are moved (eg by fork-lift truck) from the point of unloading to a storage site, if the quayside/tarmac and storage site are controlled by the same person, they would constitute one premises and would both need to be covered by the same assessment and emergency plan.

42   The situation would be different if the quayside/tarmac was a public place, under the control of another employer, or a road. If it were a public place, the REPPIR carrier provisions would apply to the fork-lift movement through that public place (see paragraphs 82 and 83 on transferring or conveying through a public place, regulation 3(1)(c)). If a road, REPPIR would not apply, but the Radioactive Material (Road Transport) (Great Britain) Regulations 1996[18] may apply.

43   Whatever radioactive substances above REPPIR threshold quantities are stored, even if these substances are stored for very short periods (as is often the case at airports), the place where they are stored is a premises to which REPPIR applies. There is no exemption for 'intermediate temporary storage', as in COMAH.

44   Vessels that are powered by nuclear reactors are to be treated as separate premises when at fixed point moorings such as buoys or alongside berths, unless they are moored at a nuclear licensed site or MoD-controlled premises in which case they are part of those premises. For emergency planning purposes at non-licensed commercial docks, it is the geographical identity of a particular vessel at a particular mooring or berth that is the key issue. For example, a vessel at a berth constitutes a premises. If that same vessel moves to a different geographical location, then this constitutes a different premises. The assessment for a particular vessel needs to underpin the off-site emergency plan for that vessel at a particular mooring or berth, and the off-site

emergency plan needs to be in place before the vessel arrives at that mooring or berth.

45   Ships and aircraft loading and unloading radioactive substances would count as transport and be covered by MCA and CAA legislation (see guidance on the definition of transport in paragraph 64).

"radiation accident" means an accident where immediate action would be required to prevent or reduce the exposure to ionising radiation of employees or any other persons and includes a radiation emergency;

46   Radiation accidents range from small occurrences, such as laboratory spillages, to so-called 'top-tier' radiation accidents, which for the purposes of REPPIR are referred to as radiation emergencies.

"radiation emergency" means any event (other than a pre-existing situation) which is likely to result in any member of the public being exposed to ionising radiation arising from that event in excess of any of the doses set out in Schedule 1 and for this purpose any health protection measure to be taken during the 24 hours immediately following the event shall be disregarded;

47   The term 'radiation emergency' is central to the interpretation of the main requirements of REPPIR and encompasses events which could reasonably be expected to lead to an emergency. Firstly, the need for operators, carriers and local authorities to prepare emergency plans (regulations 7, 8, and 9) requires a radiation emergency to be reasonably foreseeable from the operator's or carrier's work activity. Secondly, the need to supply prior information (regulation 16) similarly requires a radiation emergency to be reasonably foreseeable from the operator's or carrier's work activity. Thirdly, the local authority's prepared arrangements (regulation 17) have to cater for the distribution of information (usually prepared by other organisations) to members of the public actually affected by a radiation emergency. The extent of these duties is circumscribed by what legally constitutes a radiation emergency and the definition of this term therefore provides a measure of radiation accident severity.

48   The key element which characterises an event as a radiation emergency is the likelihood that a member of the public will be exposed to radiation doses in excess of the doses in Schedule 1 (see paragraphs 26-31 on the definition of 'member of the public'). These doses are derived from the dose limits for members of the public in the BSS96 Directive.

49   To decide whether an event satisfies the definition of a radiation emergency, certain important questions need to be answered:

(a)   Is it reasonably foreseeable that the event could lead to a radiation emergency?

(b)   Could the doses received exceed the trigger levels in Schedule 1?

(c)   Over what period would these doses be accrued?

(d)   Which 'members of the public' need to be considered?

(e)   What effect will health protection measures have on these doses?

(f)   On what technical basis should projections of dose be calculated?

Reasonably foreseeable radiation emergencies

50   The operator or carrier is responsible for assessing whether it is reasonably foreseeable that a radiation emergency may arise, although, in practice, the carrier may fulfil the duty with the assistance of the consignor. In the context of a radiation emergency, a reasonably foreseeable event would be one which was less than likely but realistically possible. The operator or carrier would be expected to have the appropriate expertise and knowledge of the (plant) operation or process concerned when assessing whether a reasonably foreseeable radiation emergency may arise. Typical issues to be considered during the assessment would be: (plant) operation limits and conditions; maintenance requirements; potential degradation mechanisms; extent of uncertainties in (plant) analysis and the safety case/review; and plant performance under external environmental and artificially induced events.

51   Emergency plans contain detailed arrangements for dealing with reasonably foreseeable radiation emergencies and provide the basis for dealing with radiation emergencies which are not reasonably foreseeable through the concept of extendibility (see paragraph 38 in the 'Emergency plans' section).

Dose levels

52   The dose levels which trigger the conditions for a radiation emergency are set out in Schedule 1. These are derived from the dose limits for members of the public (as explained in paragraph 48).

53   Operators use the Emergency Reference Levels (ERLs) from the National Radiological Protection Board (NRPB) in emergency planning. The 5 mSv dose criterion in Schedule 1 refers to projected doses over one year. In contrast, NRPB ERLs refer to dose averted during the period of the countermeasure, which would, in the case of sheltering, probably be no more than a few days. It is difficult to compare the two criteria, but, for an accident for which inhalation is the primary short-term exposure pathway, an averted dose of 3 mSv implies an outdoor inhalation dose, in the absence of sheltering, of around 6 mSv. If, in the longer term, external exposure also contributes to dose, then the 5 mSv REPPIR criterion could be viewed as somewhat more restrictive than an adoption of the lower ERL for sheltering. However, it should also be remembered that NRPB's primary advice on ERLs refers to 'a few' and 'a few tens', not specific numerical values (*Documents of the NRPB*, 1(4), page 17, Table 1[19]), and that ERLs for early countermeasures are approximate values. Given the approximate nature of the ERLs, NRPB has not considered it appropriate to modify the numerical values to match those recommended by the International Commission on Radiological Protection (5 mSv, 50 mSv etc), considering the difference to be unimportant for emergency planning purposes (see guidance on 'Effect of health protection countermeasures' in *Documents of the NRPB*, 1(4), page 17, paragraph 37;[19] and *Documents of the NRPB*, 8(1), page 10, footnote to Table 2.[20])

Time period

54   Unlike the dose limits in the 1999 Regulations, which apply to dose accrual over a calendar year, the dose levels in Schedule 1 apply to the time period of one year immediately following the radiation emergency. Therefore dose rates and intakes of radioactive substances have to be calculated over this period in determining whether the levels are likely to be exceeded.

Members of the public

55   This term is separately defined and is crucial for the correct interpretation of the definition of 'radiation emergency' (see paragraphs 26-31 on the definition of 'member of the public').

Effect of health protection measures

56   Health protection measures are intended to minimise, as far as circumstances realistically permit, the degree of radiation exposure of members of the public. The estimation of the dose to which members of the public are likely to be exposed therefore depends, in practice, not only on the accident severity, but also on the effectiveness of the health protection measures. So judgements on the effectiveness of these measures could influence whether a radiation accident comes within the definition of a radiation emergency.

57   The definition of a radiation emergency requires that the dose averted by urgent early health protection countermeasures initiated during the first 24 hours to be disregarded when projecting the dose that members of the public are likely to receive. Where there is no clearly identifiable time of the event, then this 24-hour period should be taken to start with the initiation of the emergency plan.

58   This 24-hour period is a compromise. The effectiveness of urgent early health protection countermeasures such as sheltering, distribution of tablets containing compounds of stable iodine (referred to in this guidance as 'stable iodine' tablets) and evacuation is hard to guarantee and is critically dependent on the quick co-operation of the affected population for smooth and speedy implementation (see regulations 16 and 17 on public information provision). Therefore, the emergency plan must include health protection countermeasures to be taken within the first 24 hours, but assessing the consequences of potential radiation emergencies should not take account of these early health protection countermeasures. NRPB guidance on health protection countermeasures, including 'stable iodine' tablets, is in the NRPB Board Statement on Emergency Reference Levels, *Documents of the NRPB*, 1(4) (1990).[19] While the taking of 'stable iodine' tablets is authorised by the Director of Public Health, this may be authorised in advance as part of the emergency plan, to be implemented as a result of pre-determined actions.

59   While urgent early health protection countermeasures should be disregarded, recovery measures should not, even though they may be instigated at the same time. The longer term health protection recovery measures, such as restrictions on consumption of contaminated food and drink (which are the responsibility of the Food Standards Agency), have an effect progressively over the ensuing months and years. The timescale for these measures offers a better prospect of effective implementation and it would be unrealistic to discount their effect for dose projection purposes.

Basis for dose projections

60   Well-developed modelling techniques exist which will, for any given release of radionuclides, produce projections of the dose received by individuals at defined distances from that release. The inputs to these projections will have to take into account what has been said in the preceding paragraphs, for example, about how health protection measures are to be treated.

61   However, two other parameters affect the results of these computer projections. Firstly, the dose received by an individual for a given exposure depends on that person's age group, that is, infant, child or adult. This arises from differences in metabolism and average breathing rates. For the purposes of these projections, the age group giving rise to the highest dose should be chosen.

62   The second parameter that has to be set is the weather stability category. These are defined in what are known as Pasquill categories. Category F is often used in conservative assessments, but such conditions are not common and occur mainly at night. For these reasons, and particularly because people are more likely to be indoors at night, Category F is not considered appropriate for a definition which uses the words 'likely to result in'. Category D weather is more common and more appropriate for this application, and its use is therefore recommended for modelling purposes. (Further guidance on Pasquill categories may be obtained from: the Meteorological Office website; the DEFRA website (paper on 'Selection and use of dispersion models' LAQM.TG3(00)[21]); and the NRPB website (reports from the Atmospheric Dispersion Modelling Liaison Committee (ADMLC)[22].)

2(1)

"radioactive substance" means any substance which contains one or more radionuclides whose activity cannot be disregarded for the purposes of radiation protection;

"sealed source" means a source containing any radioactive substance whose structure is such as to prevent, under normal conditions of use, any dispersion of radioactive substances into the environment;

2(1)

63   Sealed source is relevant to the definition of non-dispersible source (see paragraphs 32-35 on the definition of 'non-dispersible source'.)

"transport" means -

(a)   *carriage of a radioactive substance by rail in or on a vehicle and a radioactive substance shall be deemed as being transported from the time that it is loaded onto the vehicle for the purpose of transporting it until it is unloaded from that vehicle;*

(b)   *transferring or conveying a radioactive substance through any public place otherwise than -*

(i)   *by rail, road, inland waterway, sea or air; or*

(ii)   *by means of a pipeline or similar means;*

2(1)

64   REPPIR apply to transport operations (ie rail transport or transferring or conveying through any public place other than by standard transport modes or pipelines). Rail transport covers loading and unloading from rail vehicles. As explained in the guidance on the definition of 'premises' (ports and airports), it does not cover loading and unloading from ships and aircraft at ports and airports. This would be covered by other legislation such as the 1999 Regulations. At ports, this would also be covered by the Dangerous Substances in Harbour Areas Regulations 1987[23] (DSHAR87). At airports, loading and unloading of dangerous goods at the aircraft side should be considered as part of air transport, since an event at that time would meet the definition of a dangerous goods accident or dangerous goods incident as defined in the International Civil Aviation Organisation (ICAO) Technical Instructions.[24]

2(1)

"vehicle" means a railroad car or railway wagon, and for the purposes of these Regulations each car or wagon forming part of a larger vehicle shall be treated as a separate vehicle;

"work with ionising radiation" means work involving the production, processing, handling, use, holding, storage, transport by rail or disposal of radioactive substances which can increase the exposure of persons to radiation from an artificial source, or from a radioactive substance containing naturally occurring radionuclides which are processed for their radioactive, fissile or fertile properties.

(2) In these Regulations, any reference to a carrier is a reference to -

(a) an employer undertaking the transport by rail of any radioactive substance, and includes both a carrier for hire or reward and a carrier on own account, and

(b) an employer transferring or conveying a radioactive substance through any public place otherwise than by rail, road, inland waterway, sea or air or by means of a pipeline or similar means.

65   The term 'carrier' is used throughout these Regulations. In practice, a carrier will generally be a train operator (not an infrastructure controller) in the sense used in the 1996 Regulations, as amended. A carrier may also be an employer transferring or conveying radioactive substances through public places (but excluding by means of standard transport modes or pipelines; see guidance paragraphs 4 and 82-83 on regulation 3(1)(c)). In this document, guidance is generally (although not exclusively) for rail carriers; the principles may be relevant to employers transferring or conveying radioactive substances through public places.

(3) In these Regulations, any reference to an operator is a reference to -

(a) in relation to any premises other than a licensed site, the person who is, in the course of a trade, business or other undertaking carried on by him, in control of the operation of premises, and

(b) in relation to a licensed site, the licensee,

and any duty imposed by these Regulations on the operator shall extend only in relation to those premises.

66   The operator is the person in control of the premises. Premises generally exclude railways (see guidance on the definition of 'installation', 'premises' and 'transport' in regulation 2(1)), so an infrastructure controller is not an operator. At ports and airports, the premises usually include the storage site and sometimes also include the quayside or tarmac onto which the radioactive substances are unloaded and any intervening areas (see paragraphs 39-45 on the definition of 'premises' - ports and airports - in regulation 2(1)). At ports, the person in control of these premises is usually either the berth operator or the harbour authority, but in this document they will be referred to as the berth operator. At airports, this person is usually known as the transit shed operator and will be referred to as such.

(4) In these Regulations, unless the context otherwise requires, any reference to -

(a) an employer includes a reference to a self-employed person and any duty imposed by these Regulations on an employer in respect of his employee shall extend to a self-employed person in respect of himself;

(b) *exposure to ionising radiation is a reference to exposure to ionising radiation arising from work with ionising radiation.*

67 An employer may be:

(a) an operator;

(b) an employer working on premises under the control of an operator;

(c) a carrier;

(d) a consignor; or

(e) an employer engaged in or associated with the emergency response, on- or off-site, for example an emergency service.

(5) *Any reference in these Regulations to -*

(a) *a numbered regulation or Schedule is a reference to the regulation in or Schedule to these Regulations so numbered; and*

(b) *a numbered paragraph is a reference to the paragraph so numbered in the regulation or Schedule in which the reference appears.*

Application

68 REPPIR applies to premises or transport operations (ie rail transport or transferring or conveying through any public place, as defined in regulation 2(1)) where the quantities of radionuclides used or transported exceed those in Schedules 2 or 4, respectively, or the masses of fissile material in Schedule 3.

69 In broad terms, a radiation emergency cannot occur at premises or during transport where the work involves amounts of radionuclides that are less than or equal to the values in these Schedules. Only in situations where the amounts of radionuclides exceed these values may there be the potential for a radiation emergency to occur, and in such cases the operator or carrier must identify hazards and evaluate risks to establish whether a radiation emergency is reasonably foreseeable.

70 The radionuclides in Schedule 2 are those in the 1999 Regulations, and the quantities are derived by modelling the consequences of a worst-case release and occupancy accident scenario involving the release of radioactive substances from a premises (see NRPB report NRPB-M1311 *Calculations to assist in the revision of IRR-85 with respect to Special Hazard Assessments (REPPIR Schedule 2)).*[25]

71 The radionuclides in Schedule 4 are those for Type A packages containing radioactive material in non-special form in the International Atomic Energy Agency's (IAEA) *Regulations for the safe transport of radioactive material* TS-R-1 (revision of ST-1 1996).[26] The quantities are derived from internationally agreed transport specific accident scenarios and models. There is, consequently, no direct correlation between either the radionuclides listed in Schedules 2 and 4 or their quantities.

72 The masses of fissile material in Schedule 3 are derived from their potential to produce a criticality accident.

(1)   Subject to paragraph (4) and regulation 17, these Regulations apply to any work with ionising radiation which involves -

(a)   having on any premises or providing facilities for there to be on any premises a radioactive substance containing more than the quantity of any radionuclide specified in Schedule 2 or, in the case of fissile material, more than the mass of that material specified in Schedule 3;

(b)   transporting by rail a radioactive substance containing more than the quantity of radionuclides specified in Schedule 4 or, in the case of fissile material, more than the mass of that material specified in Schedule 3; or

(c)   transferring or conveying a radioactive substance of a quantity or mass referred to in sub-paragraph (b) above through any public place otherwise than by rail, road, inland waterway, sea or air or by means of a pipeline or similar means.

(2)   For the purposes of paragraph (1)(a), a quantity specified in Schedule 2 shall be treated as being exceeded if -

(a)   where only one radionuclide is involved, the quantity of that radionuclide exceeds the quantity specified in the appropriate entry in Part I of Schedule 2; or

(b)   where more than one radionuclide is involved, the quantity ratio calculated in accordance with Part II of Schedule 2 exceeds one.

(3)   For the purposes of paragraph (1)(b), a quantity specified in Schedule 4 shall be treated as being exceeded if -

(a)   where only one radionuclide is involved, the quantity of that radionuclide exceeds the quantity specified in the appropriate entry in Part I of Schedule 4; or

(b)   where more than one radionuclide is involved, the quantity ratio calculated in accordance with Part II of Schedule 4 exceeds one.

Application to premises

73   REPPIR apply to employers who work with ionising radiation (known in the 1999 Regulations as 'radiation employers') where the quantity of any radionuclide on the premises exceeds a specified quantity in becquerels in Part I of Schedule 2. Where there is more than one radionuclide on the premises, REPPIR will apply to those premises if the quantity ratio, calculated in accordance with the equation in Part II of Schedule 2, is greater than one. The quantities of radioactive substances are those present on the premises, including any planned increases in quantities in the facilities provided. These quantities may be different from those authorised under the Radioactive Substances Act 1993 (as amended).[27] These employers are called operators in REPPIR.

74   REPPIR will also apply to premises where the mass of any fissile material on the premises exceeds a specified quantity in grams in Schedule 3. This application relates to the potential criticality of the fissile material.

75   Premises constitute one or more installations, such as buildings and facilities where radioactive substances are produced, used, handled or stored. All the radioactive substances in all the installations (except the sources and

18

packages containing radioactive substances exempted by regulation 3(4)) must be considered when calculating the quantity ratio across the whole premises. If the quantity ratio exceeds one, then REPPIR applies. If the quantity ratio is less than or equal to one, then REPPIR does not apply. The sources and packages containing radioactive substances exempted by regulation 3(4) can be excluded from the calculation since these would not contribute to a reasonably foreseeable radiation emergency.

76   If premises change ownership the new employer/operator would have to consider the application of regulation 3 to their work activity, and if appropriate, do assessments under regulation 4.

77   Berth and transit shed operators at ports and airports will count as operators under REPPIR if they handle or store quantities of radionuclides or masses of fissile material greater than those indicated in Schedules 2 or 3, even on a temporary basis.

Application to rail transport

78   REPPIR apply to rail transport (not to transport by road, inland waterway, sea or air, for which separate legislation will apply). REPPIR will apply to employers who transport radioactive substances by rail where the quantity of any radionuclide in a vehicle (a railroad car or railway wagon) exceeds a specified quantity in becquerels in Part I of Schedule 4. Where there is more than one radionuclide in the vehicle, REPPIR will apply to that vehicle if the quantity ratio, calculated in accordance with the equation in Part II of Schedule 4, is greater than one. These employers are called carriers in REPPIR.

79   REPPIR also apply to a rail transport operation where the mass of any fissile material in a railroad car or railway wagon exceeds a specified quantity in grams in Schedule 3. This application relates to the potential criticality of the fissile material.

80   All the radioactive substances in the vehicle (except those relevant to transport described in regulation 3(4)) must be considered when calculating the quantity ratio for that vehicle, including those provided by different consignors. When considering whether REPPIR apply, only radioactive substances transported in one vehicle need be considered, not the aggregate of radioactive substances in all vehicles in the train. If the quantity ratio is less than or equal to one, then REPPIR do not apply. The sources and packages containing radioactive substances exempted by regulation 3(4) can be excluded from the calculation since these would not contribute to a reasonably foreseeable radiation emergency.

81   The most likely transport incident which may result in a radiation emergency would involve a large consignment of Type A packages containing radionuclides in non-special form. It is acknowledged that Type A packages are not normally transported by rail, but this may change in the future.

Application to public places

82   REPPIR apply to employers who transfer or convey radioactive substances through any public place, other than by the standard modes of transport or pipelines (regulation 3(1)(c)), where the quantity of any radionuclide or mass of any fissile material exceeds specified values; these values are the same as those for application to rail transport (see paragraphs 78-81 on application to rail transport). These employers are called carriers in REPPIR.

83   A public place includes public rights of way and other premises or places to which at the time in question the public have or are permitted to have access, whether on payment or otherwise. To decide whether a place is a public place, the test is whether the place in question is one where members of the public might be found and over which they might be expected to be passing or using for the purposes of access. Where use of the place is tolerated by the proprietor, that place is a public place. For ports and airports, there may be areas within its boundary which are public places and those which are not.

Application to uranium

84   Uranium commonly occurs as either natural, enriched, or depleted uranium. These terms refer to the proportion of the isotopes ^{238}U, ^{235}U, and ^{234}U in the material. Natural uranium, that is uranium as it is extracted from its ore, consists mostly of the ^{238}U isotope, with the ^{235}U and ^{234}U isotopes respectively comprising about 0.72% and 0.006% of natural uranium by mass. Enriched uranium is prepared for its fissile properties and is enriched to various degrees in the isotopes ^{235}U and ^{234}U. The process of uranium enrichment progressively removes the isotope ^{238}U from the others, so that a by-product of the process is uranium depleted in ^{235}U (and ^{234}U); this is known as depleted uranium and consists almost entirely of ^{238}U. The percentage of ^{235}U in depleted uranium is about 0.25-0.30%, with ^{234}U being present only as a trace (about 0.002%).

85   Application of REPPIR to enriched uranium will be determined by its mass, as set out in Schedule 3. For natural and depleted uranium, the quantities that determine the application of REPPIR must be taken from Schedules 2 and 4. For unirradiated natural and depleted uranium, the quantities for transport are unlimited, which means that REPPIR will not apply to the transport of such material.

86   For uranium on premises, the quantity specified in Schedule 2 for all three naturally occurring uranium isotopes is 3 GBq. This corresponds to a mass of approximately 0.2 tonnes of uranium. As newly separated (ie extracted from its ore) uranium 'ages', the activity concentration of its radioactive daughters increases and so these have to be taken into account when deciding upon the application of REPPIR (using the quantity ratio - see Part II of Schedule 2). However, most daughters take many years to achieve significant quantity activities and so can be disregarded for the purpose of REPPIR application decision-making.

87   In the case of uranium ore, all daughters will be in activity equilibrium (so-called secular equilibrium) with the uranium 'parent' and will have to be taken into account when deciding upon the application of REPPIR.

Regulation 3(4)

88   Regulation 3(4) exempts particular radioactive sources and packages containing radioactive substances on premises or during transport from the Regulations. It is highly unlikely that a radiation emergency could occur involving such sources and packages. Operators and carriers need not take account of such sources and packages when calculating the quantity ratio to establish whether REPPIR apply to their premises or transport operations (see the guidance to regulations 3(1), (2) and (3)). Assessments to identify hazards and evaluate risks from such sources and packages will be undertaken under the 1999 Regulations and MHSWR.

89 Even though these sources and packages are exempt from REPPIR, there are still requirements to prevent radiation accidents, limit consequences of radiation accidents and draw up contingency plans and rehearse them at suitable intervals under the 1999 Regulations. In addition, for transport operations involving Type B packages and consignments shipped under special arrangements for Type B packages, there are requirements for emergency plans in the 1996 Regulations. It is good practice to review and test all emergency plans.

(4)   These Regulations shall not apply in respect of -

(a)   except for the transport of such source, any non-dispersible source;

90 REPPIR do not apply to any non-dispersible source on premises. Operators who consider that a radioactive substance that they are using is non-dispersible should complete an assessment under MHSWR to confirm that this is the case, and Appendix 1 provides information on how to do this (see paragraphs 32-35 on the definition of 'non-dispersible source' in regulation 2(1)).

(b)   except for the transport of such substance, any radioactive substance which has an activity concentration of not more than 100 Bqg^{-1};

91 In relation to premises, REPPIR do not apply to any radioactive substance on premises which has an activity concentration of less than 100 Bqg^{-1}. These radioactive substances are generally naturally occurring low specific activity materials such as zircon sands.

(c)   any radioactive substance conforming to the specifications for special form radioactive material set out in the 1996 Regulations and which is certified pursuant to those Regulations as complying with them or where the transport forms part of an international transport operation as is referred to in regulation 2(3)(a), (b) or (c) of the 1996 Regulations;

92 Any radioactive substance that is special form radioactive material and which has a current certificate under the 1996 Regulations, or conforms with provisions or conditions in relevant agreements in respect of international transport operations, is exempt from REPPIR. The release of any radioactivity from such sources is highly unlikely. Such sources may be housed in Type A or Type B packages. If a source is on premises and the certificate under the 1996 Regulations has expired (or is lost and cannot be replaced), then it may still be exempt from REPPIR if that source is non-dispersible (see paragraphs 32-35 on the definition of 'non-dispersible source' in regulation 2(1)). If this is not the case, however, then that source could no longer claim exemption from REPPIR. If a source is being transported under the 1996 Regulations and the certificate has expired, then the carrier would need to transport that source in a certified Type B container (or in a Type B container under special arrangement transport operations) to continue to claim exemption from REPPIR for that source.

(d)   any radioactive substance which is in a package which complies in every respect with either the requirements for -

(i)   a Type B package design within the meaning of the 1996 Regulations; or

(ii)   a consignment shipped under Special Arrangement Transport Operations for the equivalent of a Type B package within the meaning of the 1996 Regulations, *and which is, in either case, certified pursuant to those Regulations as complying with them or where the transport forms part of an international transport operation as is referred to in regulation 2(3)(a), (b) or (c) of the 1996 Regulations;*

93   Any radioactive substance that is in a Type B package which has a current certificate under the 1996 Regulations, or conforms with provisions or conditions in relevant agreements in respect of international transport operations, is exempt from REPPIR. These packages may be on premises or being transported. The technical specification of these packages is very robust, and the release of any radioactivity from such packages is highly unlikely.

94   Any radioactive substance that is in a consignment shipped under special arrangement transport operations for the equivalent of a Type B package under the 1996 Regulations, or conforms with provisions or conditions in relevant agreements in respect of international transport operations for Type B packages, is exempt from REPPIR. These consignments under the 1996 Regulations are relatively rare, and such special arrangements are usually set up for one-off consignments where the development or acquisition of a Type B package specifically for that one-off consignment is not considered appropriate. These consignments are transported under highly specified and closely supervised conditions that should ensure that the overall level of safety is at least equivalent to that which would have been provided if the radioactive substance had been transported in a Type B package.

(e)   *the transport of any radioactive substance in the form of a low specific activity material conforming to the specifications for LSA-I, LSA-II or LSA-III within the meaning of the 1996 Regulations including cases where the transport forms part of an international transport operation as is referred to in regulation 2(3)(a), (b) or (c) of the 1996 Regulations;*

(f)   *the transport of any radioactive substance in the form of a surface contaminated object conforming to the specifications for SCO-I or SCO-II within the meaning of the 1996 Regulations including cases where the transport forms part of an international transport operation as is referred to in regulation 2(3)(a), (b) or (c) of the 1996 Regulations;*

95   The transport of any low specific activity material (LSA-I, LSA-II or LSA-III) or any surface contaminated objects (SCO-I or SCO-II) conforming to the requirements of the 1996 Regulations, including international transport operations, are exempt from REPPIR. Release of radioactive substances from such sources in sufficient quantities to result in a radiation emergency is highly unlikely.

(g)   *the presence of a radioactive substance while it is in or on the live body or corpse of a human being or animal where that presence occurs otherwise than in consequence of a radiation emergency.*

96   REPPIR does not apply to live or dead people or animals who have radioactive substances in or on their bodies during or following diagnosis or therapy involving nuclear medicine.

(5)   *These Regulations shall not apply in Northern Ireland.*

Hazard identification and risk evaluation

97   Identifying hazards, evaluating risks, and preventing accidents from occurring through appropriate control measures are fundamental to all health and safety legislation, and these requirements are included in REPPIR. Preventing radiation accidents requires a comprehensive legal framework to manage the control of exposure to ionising radiation, through a range of engineering and administrative controls, and this is provided by the 1999 Regulations which also apply to all work activities covered by REPPIR. The main purpose of REPPIR, however, is that if these control measures fail and a radiation emergency occurs, then emergency arrangements are in place which will mitigate the consequences of the emergency.

98   Regulation 4 requires operators and carriers to carry out assessments to identify the hazards and evaluate the risks from the work with ionising radiation that they propose to carry out. Having identified these hazards and risks, the operators and carriers are then required to make arrangements to prevent any radiation accident and to limit the consequences of any such accident which does occur.

(1)   *In relation to work with ionising radiation to which these Regulations apply -*

(a)   *every operator shall, before such work is for the first time carried out at the premises, make an assessment; and*

(b)   *every carrier shall before he for the first time undertakes the transport of any radioactive substance make or ensure that there has been made an assessment,*

which, in either case, is sufficient to demonstrate that -

(c)   *all hazards arising from that work with the potential to cause a radiation accident have been identified; and*

(d)   *the nature and magnitude of the risks to employees and other persons arising from those hazards have been evaluated.*

99   This regulation requires all operators and carriers to make an assessment to identify the hazards that could cause radiation accidents, including criticality accidents. Operators of berths or transit sheds may need the assistance of the consignor when making their assessments. Carriers can either make their assessments themselves or ensure that it is done by someone else (such as the consignor). The assessment should take account of both chronic and acute consequences following an accidental release of radioactive substances. Operators and carriers then have to evaluate the risks to people arising from those radiation hazards.

100   For rail transport, the safety case prepared under the RSCR should, if prepared in accordance with the relevant published HM Railway Inspectorate Assessment Criteria,[28] provide a considerable amount of the information required for the REPPIR assessment. However, the carrier may request specialist technical assistance from the consignor on the radioactive substances to be carried, possible accident scenarios and other technical information. Indeed carriers may obtain from the consignor information that they are required to provide under the 1996 Regulations or the Carriage of Dangerous Goods by Rail Regulations 1996 (CDGRR) (Part IV).[29] If carriers plan to carry radioactive substances from more than one consignor, they may need to

acquire technical information from each consignor. If they so choose, carriers may produce one assessment towards the fulfilment of their duties under all the legislation which requires such an assessment, (eg REPPIR, RSCR, the 1996 Regulations, CDGRR, the 1999 Regulations and MHSWR).

101 The assessment should cover all potential radiation accidents, which range from small occurrences to radiation emergencies (see paragraphs 47-62 on the definition of 'radiation emergency' in regulation 2(1)). The assessment should include possible plant and equipment failures, breakdown of administrative arrangements, and potential unauthorised behaviour of employees or the public. The extent and detail of the assessment should reflect the likelihood and severity of the potential radiation accident, and the findings should be recorded. The assessment should use appropriate techniques for hazard identification and risk evaluation, which in the case of potential radiation emergencies may include fault tree analysis, probabilistic safety analysis, failure modes and effects analysis, Hazard Operability Analysis (HAZOP) and Hazard Assessment Methodology (HAZAM).

102 The assessment will show whether a radiation emergency is reasonably foreseeable. For most large nuclear operations, this is likely to be the case. However, for static, non-nuclear operations, it may well be that there are no reasonably foreseeable radiation emergencies. For ports and airports, it is possible that if sufficient quantities of radioactive substances are stored (even temporarily) in storage areas controlled by berth or transit shed operators, and these premises are located near to areas to which members of the public have access, a radiation emergency at the port or airport may be reasonably foreseeable. For transport operations, the most likely scenario which may result in a radiation emergency would be a major rail transport incident involving a large consignment of Type A packages containing radionuclides in non-special form.

103 A reasonably foreseeable event would be one which is less than likely but realistically possible. When considering whether a radiation emergency is reasonably foreseeable, any urgent health protection countermeasures (such as the distribution of 'stable iodine' tablets) should be disregarded, although longer term health protection recovery measures may be taken into account (see paragraphs 50-51 on the definition of 'radiation emergency' in regulation 2(1)).

104 The value of the quantity of any radioactive substance in Schedule 2 is that which, if it were released in a radiation accident on premises, could result in members of the public receiving doses of ionising radiation in excess of those in Schedule 1. However, whether a radiation emergency could occur would depend on how much of the radioactive substance could be released at one time. If portions of the radioactive substance were kept at discrete locations around the premises (each portion containing less than the quantity in Schedule 2), then a radiation emergency could only occur if a radiation accident caused portions of radioactive substances to be released which together contained more than the quantity of radioactive substance in Schedule 2. Similarly, if the premises constituted two or more berths or transit sheds handling less than the quantity of radioactive substance in Schedule 2, a radiation emergency could only occur if these were released together and contained more than the quantity in Schedule 2.

105 The value of the quantity of any radioactive substance in Schedule 4 is that which, if it were released in a radiation accident during transport, could result in members of the public receiving doses of ionising radiation in excess of those in Schedule 1. Whether a radiation emergency could occur would

depend on how much radioactive substance could be released at one time from a single vehicle (railroad car or railway wagon).

106 The physical form of the radioactive substance is another key factor in whether a radiation accident is likely to lead to a radiation emergency. If the radioactive substance is a gas, then all of the material is likely to be released following an accident. If the radioactive substance is a liquid or dispersible solid, then only part of the material might be released during an accident. If the radioactive substance is a non-dispersible solid, then only a small part of the total quantity is likely to be released during an accident, even if that accident is a fire. If the quantity of radioactive substance likely to be released is greater than that in Schedules 2 or 4, the incident would fulfil the criteria for a potential radiation emergency. The sort of questions that need to be answered are essentially the same as those that arise when a radioactive substance is being assessed for non-dispersibility - Appendix 1 is therefore relevant.

107 Once the decision has been made as to the likely fraction of activity that would be released, the dose consequences for members of the public in the year following an atmospheric release, such as may arise as a result of a fire, can be estimated from the values tabulated in Schedules 2 and 4, as indicated in the introductory guidance to regulation 3, paragraphs 68-72. These values reflect worst-case release and occupancy scenarios (Schedule 2) and internationally agreed transport-specific accident scenarios and models (Schedule 4). For information about the personal exposure consequences of other types of release scenario, for example releases to rivers and to sewers, operators and carriers should consult NRPB report NRPB-M1311 *Calculations to assist in the revision of IRR-85 with respect to Special Hazard Assessments (REPPIR Schedule 2)*.[25]

108 Operators and carriers need to identify the consequences of any radiation emergency that is reasonably foreseeable at their premises or during transport; the likely public and worker personal exposure that may result from such events will need to be estimated so that it can be restricted and so that the need for an emergency plan (regulations 7, 8 and 9) can be established. Assessments of this kind are highly complex; operators and carriers therefore should consult their radiation protection specialist about completing these assessments (or carriers should ensure this is done).

(2) Where the assessment made for the purposes of paragraph (1) or of regulation 5 shows that a radiation risk to employees or other persons exists from an identifiable radiation accident, the operator or carrier, as the case may be, shall take all reasonably practicable steps to -

(a) prevent any such accident; and

(b) limit the consequences of any such accident which does occur.

109 All operators and carriers will have to take measures to prevent any radiation accidents identified in the assessment from occurring, and to limit the consequences of any radiation accidents which may occur.

110 The measures to prevent radiation emergencies will minimise the possibility of plant and equipment failures occurring by using, for example, plant and equipment with high technical specifications and reliability. These measures will limit the consequences of any failures by using, for example, defence in depth incorporating redundancy and diversity as appropriate. The success of administrative arrangements can be maximised by considering the

needs of employees and by providing adequate supervision of local arrangements. The extent of the measures taken to reduce the risk will reflect the likelihood and severity of the potential radiation emergency.

111   The operator or carrier should seek advice on radiation protection when making arrangements to prevent radiation accidents and to limit the consequences of any radiation accidents which may occur, or the carrier should ensure this advice is sought.

112   Relevant sections of the carrier's railway safety case may be used to satisfy the requirements of regulation 4(2).

(3)   The requirements of this regulation are without prejudice to the requirements of regulation 3 (Risk assessment) of the Management of Health and Safety at Work Regulations 1999[(a)] *and to regulation 7 (Prior risk assessment etc.) of the 1999 Regulations.*

(a) SI 1999/3242.

113   This regulation on hazard identification and risk evaluation refers to the requirements for prior risk assessment in the 1999 Regulations and for risk assessment in MHSWR. The detailed legal framework for preventing accidents by controlling exposure to ionising radiation through a range of engineering and administrative controls is provided by the 1999 Regulations.

114   Some of the requirements of REPPIR are already covered by existing nuclear site licence conditions under NIA65. These include requirements relating to hazard identification and risk evaluation (covered by the safety case). In such cases, requirements complied with under nuclear site licence conditions should satisfy equivalent requirements in REPPIR.

115   At ports and airports, any assessment carried out under REPPIR by berth or transit shed operators would complement the requirements for assessment under the 1999 Regulations (at ports and airports), DSHAR87 (at ports), and may contribute to the requirements of Civil Aviation Publication CAP 168 *Licensing of aerodromes*[30] (which places duties on airport operators at airports).

116   Some of the requirements of REPPIR are already covered by existing railway safety cases and those to be prepared under RSCR. As with nuclear sites, it will not be necessary to duplicate information and relevant documents can be used to also satisfy requirements under REPPIR or one document can be prepared to satisfy the requirements of both sets of Regulations.

Regulation 5

Review of hazard identification and risk evaluation

117   Regulation 5 requires operators and carriers to have management systems in place for the routine review of their hazard identification and risk evaluation assessments, to confirm that they are still valid. Operators and carriers should also review any material changes to their work during the review period to ensure their hazard identification and risk evaluation assessments are still valid.

(1)   Where a material change occurs in the work with ionising radiation to which an assessment made pursuant to regulation 4(1) relates -

(a)   the operator shall make a further assessment to take account of that change; and

(b)   the carrier shall make or ensure that there has been made a further assessment to take account of that change.

118   If there is a material change in the work with ionising radiation it will be necessary for the operator or carrier to assess the impact of the change on their previous assessment. Carriers must do this themselves or ensure that it is done. Such changes could include, for example:

(a)   use of different radioactive substances;

(b)   use of different quantities of the same radioactive substances;

(c)   changes in the physical form of the radioactive substances in use;

(d)   use of new or different technologies;

(e)   modifications to existing technologies; or

(f)   changes in safety management or safety-critical administrative procedures.

119   Where reviews have been carried out it is important to ensure the review has been recorded. Also where a review identifies additional hazards or an increase in risk or both, the work should be recorded.

(2)   For such time as the work with ionising radiation in respect of which an assessment made pursuant to regulation 4(1) continues, the operator and carrier shall, within 3 years of the date of the last assessment (whether made in accordance with regulation 4(1), paragraph (1) or this paragraph) either -

(a)   make (or, in relation to a carrier, ensure that there has been made) a further assessment; or

(b)   if there is no change of circumstances which would affect the last report of the assessment required by regulation 6, sign a declaration to that effect.

120   All operators and carriers must review their assessment of potential radiation accidents described in regulation 4 within at least three years of the previous assessment. Carriers must review the assessment themselves (usually with the assistance of the consignor) or ensure that the assessment is reviewed. Carriers are required to review their safety cases under RSCR at least every three years, so they may choose to carry out this review in conjunction with the review of their REPPIR assessment. Where the assessment confirms there is no change from the previous assessment then a signed declaration should be produced confirming the outcome of the review. Where an assessment which has been carried out results in either additional or fewer hazards, or an increase or decrease in risk, the work should be recorded.

Reports of assessment

121   Regulation 6 requires the operator or carrier to make arrangements for reports of their assessments (carried out under regulations 4(1), 5(1) and 5(2)) to be sent to the Executive (HSE). It also requires operators or carriers to make available to HSE reports of any further detailed assessments which may be requested. The reports submitted should contain sufficient information and appropriate cross references for HSE to confirm the outcome of the assessments. HSE will consider whether the reports have identified reasonably foreseeable radiation emergencies.

(1)   Where an assessment has been made pursuant to regulation 4(1) by an operator or carrier -

(a)   the operator in question shall send to the Executive a report of that assessment at least twelve months before the commencement of the work with ionising radiation to which the assessment relates or within such shorter time in advance as the Executive may agree; and

(b)   the carrier in question shall send to the Executive a report of that assessment at least 28 days before the commencement of the work with ionising radiation to which the assessment relates or within such shorter time in advance as the Executive may agree.

Operators

122   All operators must send a report of their assessment to HSE at least 12 months before beginning work with ionising radiation. This period would be required if the report of assessment is likely to reach the conclusion that a radiation emergency is reasonably foreseeable and that operator's and off-site emergency plans need to be prepared. A shorter period of time may be allowed with the agreement of HSE. This is likely to benefit operators where it is unlikely that a radiation emergency might occur: non-nuclear operators, including berth and transit shed operators at ports and airports, may fall into this category (see guidance paragraphs 102 and 104 on regulation 4(1) regarding non-nuclear premises). However, contingency plans under the 1999 Regulations may still be required for such operators.

123   The requirement to send a report of the assessment to HSE at least 12 months before beginning work with ionising radiation only applies to operators of new premises or operators that wish to increase their inventories to amounts above the thresholds in Schedules 2 or 3 (ie new premises in REPPIR). Operators with REPPIR quantities on site when the Regulations come into force will need to prepare an assessment within five months, in accordance with the transitional provisions in regulation 20.

Carriers

124   Carriers must send a report of assessment at least 28 days before the first transport operation. The period of 28 days can be reduced with the agreement of HSE. This assessment can be generic and does not have to be repeated before each transport operation, as long as subsequent operations are covered by the generic assessment. Carriers with assessment duties under both REPPIR and RSCR are advised to consult HM Railways Inspectorate about how to comply with both sets of Regulations in the most effective way.

125   This requirement only applies to carriers transporting radioactive substances for the first time or carriers who wish to increase their inventories to amounts above those in Schedules 3 or 4 (ie new transport operations in REPPIR). Carriers whose business included transporting REPPIR quantities before the Regulations came into force will need to prepare an assessment within five months, in accordance with the transitional provisions in regulation 20.

(2)   Where an assessment has been made pursuant to regulation 5(1), the operator or carrier in question shall send to the Executive a report of that assessment within 28 days of the making of the material change or such longer time as the Executive may agree.

126 All operators and carriers must send a report of any review of their assessment triggered by a material change to HSE within 28 days of making that change. If for any reason a longer period of time is needed, operators or carriers should inform HSE of the nature of the change that has been made and seek agreement to a delay in submitting the report. As with the original assessment for transport operations, if this material change is relevant to subsequent operations, the carrier would only need to inform HSE on the first occasion the assessment was changed (and not before subsequent operations).

(3) Where an assessment or declaration has been made pursuant to regulation 5(2), the operator or carrier in question shall send to the Executive a report of that assessment or the declaration, as the case may be, within 28 days of the assessment or declaration being made.

127 All operators must send a report of any review of their assessment or declaration triggered by the three-yearly cycle to HSE, usually within 28 days of completing that assessment. Carriers must do likewise, although they may not have undertaken the review themselves. Note that the regulation makes no provision for HSE to agree to a late report, so it is important to ensure that the report or declaration is sent promptly. HSE should be informed if operators or carriers foresee any significant delay in sending the report or declaration.

(4) A report of an assessment made for the purposes of this regulation shall include the particulars specified in Schedule 5.

128 The report of the assessment must include the issues in Schedule 5 (see guidance on Schedule 5). The assessment should be sufficient to show whether a radiation emergency is reasonably foreseeable.

129 For a nuclear licensed site regulated under NIA65 these requirements should be met by the requirements of the nuclear site licence.

(5) Where, for the purpose of assessing the risk to health or safety of persons who could be affected by work with ionising radiation to which regulation 4 applies, the Executive may reasonably require a detailed assessment of any of the further particulars set out in Schedule 6, it may, by notice in writing served on the operator or carrier, require him to carry out (or, in relation to a carrier, require him to ensure that there has been carried out) such detailed assessment of such matters as are specified in the notice and the operator or carrier, as the case may be, shall send a report of that assessment to the Executive within such time as is specified in the notice or within such longer time as the Executive may subsequently allow.

130 If the hazard identification and risk evaluation required by regulation 4 lead the operator or carrier to conclude that there is a significant risk of a radiation emergency arising from their work activities, HSE may require a further assessment to be carried out on any of the issues in Schedule 6, in accordance with regulation 6(5), and any such request will be in writing (see guidance on Schedule 6). This further assessment will be expected to address uncertainties in the methodologies used and the impact of those uncertainties on the effectiveness of measures taken to prevent and control any potential radiation emergency.

131 For a nuclear licensed site regulated under NIA65, these requirements should be met by the requirements of the nuclear site licence.

Emergency plans

132 This section on guidance on emergency plans is relevant to regulations 7, 8, 9 and 10, that is on the preparation of emergency plans and their review and testing. The guidance gives a broad overview of the production and use of emergency plans, and of the need to address public health aspects of radiation emergencies in consultation on, and preparation of, emergency plans. These matters are also covered in greater detail in the NEPLG consolidated guidance document.[15]

Production of emergency plans

133 The emergency plan is a document that explains the principles by which a reasonably foreseeable radiation emergency will be handled. It describes roles and responsibilities of emergency response organisations and may be supported by other detailed documentation describing the detailed arrangements.

134 Emergency plans should be based on the specific needs of each particular premises or possible transport scenario. Emergency plans should address the full range of reasonably foreseeable radiation emergencies and the arrangements for dealing with those emergencies. The degree of planning should be proportional to the probability of the accident occurring (see paragraphs 50-51 on the definition of 'radiation emergency' in regulation 2(1) regarding reasonably foreseeable radiation emergencies.)

135 Some components of the emergency plan are primarily about the response, for example:

(a)   when and how to call the emergency services;

(b)   who will take charge and what they will be responsible for;

(c)   relevant procedures for the response;

(d)   special procedures for dealing with particular circumstances;

(e)   availability of resources including the requirement for any specialist equipment;

(f)   where and how to get information;

(g)   how the emergency responders can be easily identified including how they can identify each other;

(h)   where the emergency responders will be able to rendezvous and how they will communicate.

136 Other components of the emergency planning arrangements will be primarily about making the emergency plan work and may be documented separately from the plan, for example:

(a)   training for emergency planners;

(b)   training for people with roles to play in connection with the plan;

(c)   how plan components will be tested;

(d)   how plan components will be updated;

(e)   how plan components will be reviewed and revised to take account of changes or lessons learned.

137   The documentation should be a record of agreements and procedures which cover all the appropriate people and organisations, and all the necessary resources for the full range of reasonably foreseeable radiation emergency situations anticipated.

138   It is good practice for the emergency plan also to provide the basis for dealing with radiation emergencies that are not reasonably foreseeable through the concept of extendibility. The emergency plan should be extendible to provide rapid and effective mitigation for radiation emergencies which could occur, but the likelihood of which is so remote that detailed emergency planning against their consequences is not justified. Further guidance on extendibility is available in *Arrangements for responding to nuclear emergencies*[16] and the NEPLG consolidated guidance document[15] (see chapters on 'Emergency plans' and 'Early countermeasures beyond the detailed emergency planning zone').

139   The emergency plan should address the response required during all the phases of the emergency, both the immediate needs and longer term recovery, but focusing on the first few hours after the accident occurs. This is the 'critical' phase of an accident response, when key decisions, which will greatly affect the success of any mitigation measures, must be made within a short period of time and when those responsible will be under considerable pressure. Therefore, an understanding of the likely sequence of events and appropriate countermeasures is of great benefit for all those who may reasonably be expected to have a role to play.

140   A large part of the emergency plan preparation is about the exchange of information and ideas between people and organisations. Serious consideration should be given to the most effective way of carrying this out for the circumstances of a particular emergency plan. There are numerous possible approaches. In addition to the obvious communication methods, via telephone letter and fax, there are:

(a)   steering groups;

(b)   emergency planning working groups;

(c)   meetings of a selection of the organisations involved;

(d)   discussion or focus groups; and

(e)   briefing or review meetings.

141   There are positive benefits of providing clear and timely information to broadcast and printed media as an important method of informing the public during a radiation emergency, and also providing important reassurance where this is appropriate. For more information, see the Home Office publication *Dealing with disaster*[11] and its Scottish equivalent *Dealing with disasters together.*[12] Specific advance consideration should be given to the formulation of links between those delegated to manage media relations on behalf of the various response agencies. This should ensure that any statements released to the media and public on issues, including public health, are jointly agreed and approved by all parties. This also includes information provided through public help-lines.

Use of emergency plans

142 Emergency plans are live documents. They should be kept up to date and put into effect without delay whenever needed, and all those with agreed roles and responsibilities should carry them out when, where and how they have been agreed.

143 The principles outlined in the emergency plan should be followed during training, testing and implementing the plan. It is helpful to include checklists in the plan as a guide to informed decision-making and as a series of reminders for individuals.

144 The emergency plan should include arrangements for:

(a) bringing together the people who would have to deal with a radiation emergency to assess the possible consequences and implement co-ordinated response procedures;

(b) alerting contacts both in and out of working hours; and

(c) ensuring provision of information to the public who might be affected by a radiation emergency.

Public health aspects of radiation emergencies

145 In developing the public health related components of their respective plans and in seeking to achieve integrated emergency management, operators, carriers and local authorities will need to consult with health authorities/boards and ambulance trusts, and jointly agree respective roles and responsibilities (see chapter in the NEPLG consolidated guidance document[15] on 'Roles and responsibilities of responding organisations'). Health authorities/boards will also consult, or facilitate consultation with, the appropriate hospital and emergency units and acute hospital trusts.

146 Procedures will also need to be considered and jointly agreed for activation of the various component parts of the National Health Service (NHS), including the identification of relevant post holders from each health authority/board or trust to attend strategic, tactical and operational control centres/points, where appropriate. It may be prudent for health authorities/boards to consider strategies and back-up plans if one health authority/board were to be overwhelmed by the number of casualties arising from an incident.

147 The public health aspects of an accident involving a radiation emergency are likely to continue during the recovery phase (see chapter in the NEPLG consolidated guidance document on 'Procedures for recovery').

148 Operators, carriers and local authorities will also need to work closely with health authorities/boards and ambulance trusts, as well as with the emergency services, government agencies and other key organisations, in considering when and where treatment of casualties and response personnel should take place, and in determining arrangements for establishing the level of personal protective equipment needed for the use of response and medical personnel.

149 More specifically, local authorities will also need to discuss with health authorities/boards and the relevant voluntary aid societies, the inclusion of arrangements within their own emergency response arrangements for

managing the health care needs of individuals who have been evacuated. The arrangements may include access to routine medications if evacuation is prolonged, and the provision of services to support people suffering from stress-related conditions as a result of the incident.

Operator's emergency plan

(1)   Where the assessment made by an operator in accordance with regulation 4(1) or regulation 5 shows that it is reasonably foreseeable that a radiation emergency might arise (having regard to the steps taken by the operator under regulation 4(2)), the operator shall prepare an adequate emergency plan (in these Regulations referred to as an "operator's emergency plan") designed to secure, so far as is reasonably practicable, the restriction of exposure to ionising radiation and the health and safety of persons who may be affected by such reasonably foreseeable emergencies as are identified by the said assessment.

150   As with assessments, the duty to prepare an emergency plan for premises is placed on the operator, although the operator of a berth or transit shed may need the assistance of the consignor when preparing the emergency plan.

151   The hazard identification and risk evaluation required by regulation 4 will show whether a radiation emergency is reasonably foreseeable. If the assessment shows that it is not reasonably foreseeable for a radiation emergency to occur at the premises, then the operator will not have to prepare an operator's emergency plan under REPPIR. The operator will still have to prepare a contingency plan under the 1999 Regulations to deal with radiation accidents which may occur.

152   If the assessment under regulation 4 shows that a radiation emergency could occur at the premises, then the operator will have to prepare a written emergency plan under REPPIR to deal with any reasonably foreseeable radiation emergency (see paragraphs 50-51 on the definition of 'radiation emergency' in regulation 2(1) regarding reasonably foreseeable radiation emergencies). The emergency plan can take account of measures taken by the operator to prevent radiation emergencies from occurring, and measures taken to limit their consequences if they should occur. The degree of planning should be proportional to the probability of the accident occurring. Detailed planning to manage a reasonably foreseeable radiation emergency would be used as a framework to respond to a very low frequency, high consequence radiation emergency which is not reasonably foreseeable, through the concept of extendibility (see paragraph 138 of the 'Emergency plans' section).

153   Operators who must prepare emergency plans under other legislation, such as COMAH, may choose to prepare an integrated operator's emergency plan covering a range of radiation and chemical or other hazards. An effective operator's emergency plan could, therefore, satisfy the requirements of more than one set of regulations (eg contingency plans in the 1999 Regulations and emergency plans in REPPIR and COMAH).

154   Some of the requirements of REPPIR are already covered by existing nuclear site licence conditions under NIA65 (eg the operator's emergency plan is covered by the emergency arrangements). For a nuclear licensed site regulated under NIA65, these requirements should be met by the requirements of the nuclear site licence. REPPIR will not replace existing nuclear site licence conditions, but compliance with the conditions should satisfy equivalent provisions in REPPIR.

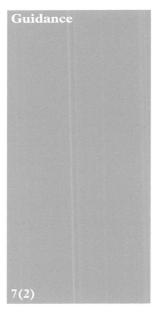
155　Berth operators at ports will need to comply with DSHAR87 and the 1999 Regulations which require them to have emergency arrangements or contingency plans in place, respectively. DSHAR87 also require harbour authorities to have on-site emergency plans covering the whole port. If REPPIR apply and the assessment shows that emergency plans are required, it is likely that the operators' and off-site emergency plans required by REPPIR would satisfy the requirements of these other sets of Regulations. (Also see paragraph 296 on regulation 11(3) regarding co-operation relating to berth and transit shed operators.)

156　Similarly, transit shed operators at airports will need to co-operate with airport operators' contingency plans drawn up under CAP 168 licence conditions and develop contingency plans under the 1999 Regulations. Emergency plans prepared under REPPIR could help transit shed operators achieve this, if only partially. (Also see paragraphs 296 on regulation 11(3) regarding co-operation relating to transit shed operators.)

157　The operator's emergency plan covers all operator's actions, both those on-site and assisting with off-site mitigatory action (see Schedule 7). For example, the operator assists with off-site monitoring; further guidance is available in the NEPLG consolidated guidance document.

158　The operator's emergency plan should allow for the provision of possible reductions in staffing levels or closure of facilities during weekends, public holidays etc. This is to ensure the plan considers reasonably foreseeable situations when routine staffing levels may not be available.

159　The operator should seek advice on radiation protection, as appropriate, at all relevant stages of the emergency planning process (see introductory guidance to regulation 14(1) paragraphs 335 and 340).

160　The operator is required to supply necessary information to the local authority to enable the off-site emergency plan to be prepared (see regulations 9(4), (5) and (6)).

7(1)

**Regulation
7(2)**

(2)　*Without prejudice to paragraph (1), the operator's emergency plan shall contain the information specified in Part I of Schedule 7.*

Guidance

161　The operator should ensure that the emergency plan contains all the information required by Part I of Schedule 7. The plan details the roles that those who work on the premises will have to play in the event of a radiation emergency. It should also be supported by arrangements that are established for assisting with emergency response off-site. The plan must dovetail with the off-site emergency plan, so that the emergency services and those responsible for communicating information to those outside the premises know where and in what form they will receive information (see paragraphs 314-320 on the implementation of emergency plans in regulation 13).

162　The operator's emergency plan must establish the system for managing information in the event of a radiation emergency. This should ensure that necessary information can be identified and communicated to people on-site, the emergency services and other organisations identified in the plan as having a role to play and requiring information. Even where a radiation emergency has not yet resulted in off-site consequences, there are considerable benefits in keeping members of the public in the vicinity of the premises informed about what is happening. The operator also has a duty to provide information to the public (see regulation 16).

7(2)

(3)   No person shall carry out work with ionising radiation to which the assessment made in accordance with regulation 4(1) applies unless -

(a)   the operator has complied with the requirements of paragraphs (1) and (2); and

(b)   the local authority has complied with the requirements of regulation 9(1), (2), (8) and (9) and has provided confirmation of this to the operator in accordance with regulation 9(13).

Guidance

7(3)

163   If the operator is required by REPPIR to prepare an emergency plan, then the operator must not begin work with ionising radiation under REPPIR until both the operator's emergency plan and the off-site emergency plan have been prepared (see regulations 9(9) and (13)). For transitional provisions when REPPIR comes into force, however, see regulation 20(2)(b).

Regulation
7(4)

(4)   The operator's emergency plan shall be drawn up having regard to the principles set out in Part I of Schedule 8.

Guidance

7(4)

164   The operator's emergency plan must be drawn up taking account of the principles of intervention in Part I of Schedule 8. Intervention strategies will have to weigh up the benefits (advantages) of proposed intervention against the detriments (harm) of that intervention, and make sure that the benefits from intervention outweigh the detriments. Social costs (eg costs involved for the local population if they need to be evacuated) have to be taken into account as part of the detriment of intervention.

165   In REPPIR, emergency preparedness requires that provision be made to reduce the transfer of radioactive substances to people from the environment. Steps taken to protect human health may also provide much protection for the environment. Nevertheless, attention should be paid to the environmental harm which could result from a particular emergency intervention. Such harm would form part of the social cost and the detriment associated with the intervention, as referred to in sub-paragraphs (a) and (b) of Part I of Schedule 8. Remedial measures can affect the radioactive waste arising from a radiation emergency, and handling such waste may also contribute to costs to society.

Regulation
7(5)

(5)   Without prejudice to the generality of paragraph (1), the operator's emergency plan shall secure, where appropriate, intervention for the purposes set out in Part II of Schedule 8.

Guidance

7(5)

166   The operator's emergency plan must be drawn up taking account of the purposes of intervention in Part II of Schedule 8. The operator has a role to play in each of the purposes described:

(a)   the operator has a key role in reducing or stopping the release of radioactive substances from the premises. The operator's emergency plan should describe the measures and arrangements to do this;

(b)   the operator can advise off-site agencies on the quantities of radioactive substances released and the level and location of contamination off-site, so that those agencies can take steps to restrict the exposure of the public from radioactive substances in the environment. The operator's emergency plan should describe arrangements to do this;

(c)   the operator's emergency plan should describe arrangements to restrict the exposure of employees and others on the premises. The operator can advise off-site agencies on the nature of the radioactive substances released and on determining the level of exposure of people to ionising radiation, including personal contamination, so that those agencies can organise effective medical treatment of people. The operator's emergency plan should describe arrangements to do this. The medical treatment is relevant to both on- and off-site, although it is more likely to be for on-site casualties.

(6) For the purpose of preparing the operator's emergency plan pursuant to paragraph (1) or of reviewing the plan pursuant to regulation 10(1), the operator shall consult –

(a) his employees, any person carrying out work on behalf of the operator, the Executive, the local authority in whose area the premises of the operator are situated, the emergency services, the health authority for the area in which the premises of the operator are situated and the Agency; and

(b) such other persons, bodies and authorities as the operator considers appropriate,

and, in a case where the emergency services form part of the plan, shall give such information to those services as will enable them to perform their functions in accordance with the plan.

167   Employees identified as having a role to play in the emergency response to a radiation emergency should be consulted during the preparation, review and revision of the operator's emergency plan. There are legal requirements to consult with employees under the Safety Representatives and Safety Committees Regulations 1977 and the Health and Safety (Consultation with Employees) Regulations 1996. As well as those employed directly by the operator, consultation should include others who normally work on the premises, for example contractors' employees. Consultation with employees and with contractors' employees may be direct or through appointed employee representatives.

168   The operator should identify all the organisations that need to be consulted in the preparation of the operator's emergency plan. This will always include HSE, the local authority, emergency services, health authority/board, and relevant Agency.

169   Consultation with the local authority will be on the aspects of the operator's emergency plan in which off-site agencies have a role, and which have interfaces with the off-site emergency plan. This is to ensure adequate dovetailing between the two emergency plans which apply to the premises.

170   Emergency services identified as having a role to play in the emergency response on the premises must be consulted to reach agreement on the role that they would perform in the event of a radiation emergency. Discussions should include radiation protection arrangements for emergency services personnel responding to such an emergency (see paragraphs 293-295 on consultation and co-operation in regulation 11, and paragraphs 370-379 on dose levels for emergency exposures in regulation 14.)

171   The operator must consult the health authority/board for the area in the vicinity of their premises on the nature of the radioactive substances on the premises, so that the health authority/board can plan for the treatment of people who may be affected by a radiation emergency. Health authorities/boards are responsible for ensuring that satisfactory arrangements are in place for handling the health care aspects of the response to a radiation emergency. This will include ensuring arrangements are in place with acute hospital trusts and other trusts responsible for managing primary and

community care for the treatment of any casualties that may arise and determining, where appropriate, the most suitable holding locations for supplies of up-to-date stocks of health care products.

172 The operator must consult the relevant Agency, in particular regarding the management, including disposal of, radioactive waste arising from a radiation emergency; this would be the Environment Agency (EA) for premises in England and Wales or the Scottish Environment Protection Agency (SEPA) for premises in Scotland.

173 It may also be necessary to consult with other organisations who might be involved with or affected by implementation of the operator's emergency plan (eg water authorities/suppliers).

174 Berth or transit shed operators should consult with harbour authorities or airport operators on the operator's emergency plan.

(7) The operator shall ensure that any employee who may be involved with or may be affected by arrangements in the operator's emergency plan is or has been provided with -

(a) suitable and sufficient information, instruction and training; and

(b) the equipment necessary to restrict that employee's exposure to ionising radiation including, where appropriate, the issue of suitable dosemeters or other devices obtained in either case from the approved dosimetry service with which the operator has entered into an arrangement under regulation 21 of the 1999 Regulations.

175 The purpose of regulation 7(7) is a general requirement for training and equipment for intervention personnel and for non-intervention personnel (eg office staff). It applies whether or not emergency exposures are required (see guidance on regulations 14(1)(b), (c) and (g) regarding training and equipment when intervention personnel may receive emergency exposures).

176 Employees involved in intervention should be given appropriate training on how to fulfil their roles in the operator's emergency plan. Refresher training should be provided as appropriate. Arrangements should be in place to make sure that equipment necessary for intervention will be available during a radiation emergency, and that dosemeters (or other devices that may be used to determine radiation exposure) are also available from an approved dosimetry service. Some employees may be provided with routine dosimetry under the 1999 Regulations, and the operator should consider, in consultation with the approved dosimetry service, whether to make arrangements to issue additional dosemeters in the event of a radiation emergency occurring (assuming that there is enough time to do this).

177 The operator should make sure that all non-intervention personnel working on their premises, including those of other employers, are given suitable and sufficient information and instruction on what to do in the event of a radiation emergency. This information may need to be repeated on an appropriate regular basis, and there should be arrangements in place to make sure that all employees new to the premises are given information and instruction.

178 The operator will also need to provide suitable and sufficient information and instruction to visitors who are on the premises, as and when appropriate. This includes patients attending or visiting hospitals, and students attending educational or research establishments (see paragraphs 26-31 on the definition of 'member of the public' in regulation 2(1)).

(8)   The operator shall provide to the Executive upon request and within such reasonable time as the Executive may specify a copy of the operator's emergency plan or such parts of that plan as the Executive may require.

179   HSE may request a copy of the operator's emergency plan or parts of the plan. There is no need to routinely send a copy of the operator's emergency plan to HSE without being asked to do so.

Regulation 8

Carrier's emergency plan

(1)   Where the assessment made in accordance with regulation 4(1) or regulation 5 shows that it is reasonably foreseeable that a radiation emergency might arise in respect of the transport of a radioactive substance (having regard to the steps taken by the carrier under regulation 4(2)), the carrier shall prepare or ensure that there has been prepared an adequate emergency plan in respect of the transport of such substances (in these Regulations referred to as a "carrier's emergency plan") designed to secure, so far as is reasonably practicable, the restriction of exposure to ionising radiation and the health and safety of persons who may be affected by such reasonably foreseeable emergencies as are identified by the said assessment.

180   As with assessments, the duty to prepare an emergency plan for certain transport operations is placed on the carrier or for the carrier to ensure that this is done; the carrier may ask the consignor to prepare or at least provide a substantial contribution to the emergency plan.

181   The hazard identification and risk evaluation required by regulation 4 will show whether a radiation emergency is reasonably foreseeable. If the assessment shows that it is not reasonably foreseeable for a radiation emergency to occur during transport, then the carrier will not have to prepare a carrier's emergency plan under REPPIR or ensure one is prepared. The carrier will still have to prepare a contingency plan under the 1999 Regulations to deal with radiation accidents which may occur and make suitable emergency arrangements under the 1996 Regulations and RSCR.

182   If the assessment under regulation 4 shows that a radiation emergency could occur during transport, then the carrier will have to prepare a written emergency plan under REPPIR to deal with any reasonably foreseeable radiation emergency, or ensure that an emergency plan is prepared (see paragraphs 50-51 on the definition of 'radiation emergency' in regulation 2(1) regarding reasonably foreseeable radiation emergencies). The emergency plan can take account of measures taken by the carrier to prevent radiation emergencies, and measures taken to limit their consequences if they should occur. The degree of planning should be proportional to the probability of the accident occurring. The plan is likely to be generic in nature, and sufficiently flexible to be able to handle any potential radiation emergency wherever it may occur.

183   Carriers who must prepare contingency or emergency plans under other legislation, such as the 1999 Regulations, 1996 Regulations or RSCR, may choose to prepare an integrated carrier's emergency plan covering a range of radiation or other hazards. An effective carrier's emergency plan could, therefore, satisfy the requirements of more than one set of regulations. Most current rail transport operations (usually Type B packages) would be covered by the 1996 Regulations and not by REPPIR. An emergency plan prepared under REPPIR, however, may be more detailed that that specified by the 1996 Regulations, so the REPPIR plan would probably satisfy the requirements of those Regulations. National transport plans exist which could form the basis of

the rail carrier's emergency plan (eg RADSAFE, if the carrier or the consignor was a member of the RADSAFE scheme[31]).

184 The carrier's emergency plan should allow for the provision of possible reductions in staffing levels or closure of central facilities during weekends, public holidays etc. This is to ensure the plan considers reasonably foreseeable situations when routine staffing levels may not be available.

185 The carrier (or consignor acting on their behalf) should seek advice on radiation protection, as appropriate, at all relevant stages of the emergency planning process (see introductory guidance to regulation 14, paragraphs 335-344).

(2) Without prejudice to paragraph (1), the carrier's emergency plan shall contain the information specified in Part II of Schedule 7.

186 The carrier's emergency plan will contain, in principle, information on similar issues to those in an operator's emergency plan. In practice, however, the plan is likely to be generic in nature, and the way that particular issues are handled (such as dose assessments) are likely to be quite different. The carrier (or the person who prepares the plan on behalf of the carrier) should ensure that the plan contains all the information required by Part II of Schedule 7.

187 The carrier's emergency plan must establish a system for managing information in the event of a radiation emergency. This should ensure that necessary information can be identified and communicated to people at central headquarters, the emergency services and other organisations identified in the plan as having a role to play and requiring information. Even when a transport incident has occurred but there has not been a release of radioactive substances, there are considerable benefits in keeping those in the vicinity of the incident informed about what is happening. The carrier also has a duty to provide prior information to the public (see regulation 16).

(3) A carrier shall not undertake the transport of any radioactive substance to which the assessment made in accordance with regulation 4(1) applies unless he has complied with the requirements of paragraph (1) and (2).

188 If the carrier is required by REPPIR to prepare an emergency plan or ensure that one is prepared, then the carrier must not transport radioactive substances under REPPIR until that plan has been prepared. For transitional provisions when REPPIR comes into force, however, see regulation 20(2)(6).

(4) Where not also the carrier, the consignor shall, before presenting a consignment of any radioactive substance for transport, supply to the carrier such information as is necessary for the purpose of enabling the carrier to prepare or ensure that there is prepared the carrier's emergency plan required by this regulation.

189 There is a duty on the consignor to provide information to the carrier to enable the carrier's emergency plan to be prepared. The consignor and carrier may be in the same organisation. The consignor may also be the person preparing the emergency plan on behalf of the carrier.

190 For transport operations under a carrier's emergency plan, the carrier needs to know details of the radioactive substances to be transported before they are collected, so that the carrier can check that their emergency plan will be adequate to handle any transport incident and radiation emergency which may occur. Since the emergency plan is likely to be generic, any minor amendment to the plan for any particular consignment is likely to be rare. The information that the consignor should supply before transport would include

details of: the radioactive substances; the amounts (in becquerels) to be transported; and the type of packaging. It is important to emphasise that the consignor should allow sufficient time for the carrier to assess the information provided and to confirm the adequacy of the plan.

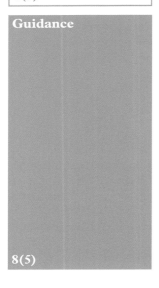

Regulation

8(5)

(5)   The carrier's emergency plan shall be drawn up having regard to the principles set out in Part I of Schedule 8.

Guidance

191   The carrier's emergency plan must be drawn up taking account of the principles of intervention in Part I of Schedule 8. Intervention strategies will have to weigh up the benefits (advantages) of proposed intervention against the detriments (harm) of that intervention, and make sure that the benefits from intervention outweigh the detriments. Social costs (eg costs involved for the local population if they need to be evacuated) have to be taken into account as part of the detriment of intervention.

192   In REPPIR, emergency preparedness requires that provision be made to reduce the transfer of radioactive substances to people from the environment. Steps taken to protect human health may also provide much protection for the environment. Nevertheless, attention should be paid to the environmental harm which could result from a particular emergency intervention. Such harm would form part of the social cost and the detriment associated with the intervention, as referred to in sub-paragraphs (a) and (b) of Part I of Schedule 8. Remedial measures can affect the radioactive waste arising from a radiation emergency, and handling such waste may also contribute to costs to society.

8(5)

Regulation

8(6)

(6)   Without prejudice to the generality of paragraph (1), the carrier's emergency plan shall secure, where appropriate, intervention for the purposes set out in Part II of Schedule 8.

Guidance

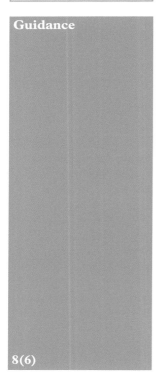

193   The carrier's emergency plan must be drawn up taking account of the purposes of intervention in Part II of Schedule 8. The carrier has a role to play in each of the purposes described:

(a)   the carrier has a key role in reducing or stopping the release of radioactive substances from its transport containment. The carrier's emergency plan should describe the measures and arrangements to do this;

(b)   the carrier can advise external agencies on the quantities of radioactive substances released and the level and location of contamination around the transport incident, so that those agencies can take steps to restrict the exposure of the public from radioactive substances in the environment. The carrier's emergency plan should describe arrangements to do this;

(c)   the carrier's emergency plan should describe arrangements to restrict the exposure of employees and others during a transport incident. The carrier can advise external agencies on the nature of the radioactive substances released and on determining the level of exposure of people to ionising radiation, including personal contamination, so that those agencies can organise effective medical treatment of people. The consignor may assist the carrier in providing such advice. The carrier's emergency plan should describe arrangements to do this.

8(6)

Regulation

(7)   For the purpose of preparing a carrier's emergency plan pursuant to paragraph (1) or of reviewing the plan pursuant to regulation 10(1), the carrier shall ensure that consultation is carried out with -

(a)   the Executive, (where not also the carrier) the consignor and the Agency; and

8(7)

(b)   such local authorities, emergency services, health authorities and other persons, bodies or authorities (or in each case representatives thereof) as the carrier considers appropriate.

194   Consultation should be carried out when the carrier's emergency plan is being prepared or revised. Consultation before each transport operation is not necessary. Consultation requirements also apply to foreign carriers operating in Great Britain.

195   The carrier (or person who prepares the plan on behalf of the carrier) should identify all the organisations that need to be consulted in the preparation of the carrier's emergency plan. This will always include HSE, the relevant Agency and consignor (where not also the carrier).

196   The carrier needs to consult consignors on the carrier's emergency plan. As the emergency plan is likely to be generic, the dialogue between the carrier and consignor on the nature of the radioactive substances to be carried may include potential future transport operations, and should be sufficient to enable the carrier to be sure that their emergency plan is adequate for all foreseeable future transport operations.

197   The carrier must consult the relevant Agency, in particular regarding the management, including disposal of, radioactive waste arising from a radiation emergency; this would be EA for transport operations in England and Wales, and SEPA for transport operations in Scotland. In the case of transport across the border between England and Scotland, both Agencies must be consulted.

198   The carrier needs to consult local authorities, emergency services and health authorities/boards, as appropriate, on their emergency plan. The intention is not to consult each and every local authority, emergency service and health authority/board along recognised rail routes for radioactive substances if REPPIR is likely to apply, but rather to consult with representatives of such bodies. This consultation, which is likely to be at a national level, would be on a generic emergency plan which could be used for any route, although recognised rail routes should be specified. These could include national representatives of a range of organisations such as (in alphabetical order):

(a)   Ambulance Service Association (ASA);

(b)   Association of Chief Police Officers (ACPO) and ACPO Scotland;

(c)   Chief and Assistant Chief Fire Officers Association (CACFOA);

(d)   Convention of Scottish Local Authorities (COSLA);

(e)   Department of Health (DoH), Scottish Executive Health Department (SEHD), the NHS Executive (in England, Wales and Scotland);

(f)   DTI's Nuclear Emergency Planning Liaison Group (NEPLG);

(g)   Emergency Planning Society (EPS);

(h)   HM Coastguard;

(i)   Local Government Association (LGA).

199   Some of these national representatives can be contacted via NEPLG.

Guidance

8(7)

200 General civil defence (emergency) plans, which local authorities already have in place, should be capable of dealing with much of the impact of a transport radiation accident or emergency, as with other types of emergency (eg a major chemical spillage). These local authority plans, however, are not a substitute for the carrier's emergency plan, but will complement it.

201 The carrier may need to consult other organisations; rail carriers will generally need to consult the infrastructure controller. Other consultees for the carrier's emergency plan could include water authorities/suppliers. Consultation with employees is also required by the Safety Representatives and Safety Committees Regulations 1977 and the Health and Safety (Consultation with Employees) Regulations 1996.

Regulation

8(8)

(8) The carrier shall ensure that any employee under his control who may be involved with or may be affected by arrangements in the carrier's emergency plan is or has been provided with -

(a) suitable and sufficient information, instruction and training; and

(b) the equipment necessary to restrict that employee's exposure to ionising radiation including, where appropriate, suitable dosemeters or other devices obtained in either case from the approved dosimetry service with which the carrier has entered into an arrangement under regulation 21 of the 1999 Regulations.

Guidance

8(8)

202 The purpose of regulation 8(8) is a general requirement for training and equipment for intervention personnel and for non-intervention personnel (eg headquarters staff). It applies whether or not emergency exposures are required (see guidance on regulations 14(1)(b), (c) and (g) regarding training and equipment when intervention personnel may receive emergency exposures).

203 Employees involved in intervention should be given appropriate training on how to fulfil their roles in the carrier's emergency plan. Refresher training should be provided, as appropriate. Arrangements should be in place to make sure that equipment necessary for intervention will be made available during a radiation emergency, and that dosemeters (or other devices that may be used to determine radiation exposure) will also be made available from an approved dosimetry service under the 1999 Regulations. Equipment and dosemeters or other devices may be present during travel or held elsewhere (such as at a central or regional depot).

204 The carrier should make sure that all non-intervention personnel involved in their transport operations, including those of other employers, are given suitable and sufficient information and instruction on what to do in the event of a radiation emergency. This information may need to be repeated on an appropriate regular basis, and there should be arrangements in place to make sure that all employees new to the transport operations are given information and instruction.

Regulation

8(9)

(9) Where requested by the Executive, the carrier shall provide to the Executive within such reasonable time as may be specified a copy of the carrier's emergency plan or such parts of the plan as the Executive may require.

Guidance

8(9)

205 HSE may request a copy of the carrier's emergency plan or parts of the plan. There is no need to routinely send a copy of the carrier's emergency plan to HSE without being asked to do so.

Off-site emergency plan

(1)   The local authority in whose area there is situated premises at which there is carried out work with ionising radiation to which these Regulations apply and in respect of which an assessment made by the operator pursuant to regulation 4(1) or regulation 5 shows that it is reasonably foreseeable that a radiation emergency might arise (having regard to the steps taken by the operator under regulation 4(2)) shall prepare an adequate emergency plan (in these Regulations referred to as an "off-site emergency plan") designed to secure, so far as is reasonably practicable, the restriction of exposure to ionising radiation and the health and safety of persons who may be affected by such reasonably foreseeable emergencies as are identified in that assessment and the plan shall be prepared in respect of such area as in the opinion of the Executive any member of the public is likely to be affected by such radiation emergencies.

206   The local authority must prepare a written off-site emergency plan for any premises with an operator's emergency plan (see paragraphs 22-25 on the definition of 'local authority' in regulation 2(1)). HSE determines the area of the emergency planning zone under regulation 9(1) and the area of the public information zone under regulation 16(1). The off-site emergency plan can take account of measures taken by the operator to prevent radiation emergencies, and measures taken to limit their consequences if they should occur. As with the operator's emergency plan, the degree of planning should be proportional to the probability of an accident occurring. Detailed planning to manage a reasonably foreseeable radiation emergency could be used as a framework also to respond to a very low frequency, high consequence radiation emergency which is not reasonably foreseeable through the concept of extendibility (see paragraph 138 in the 'Emergency plans' section). Note that there is no requirement for local authorities to prepare emergency plans for transport under REPPIR.

207   The off-site emergency plan is an integrated emergency management plan to bring together the emergency arrangements of all the off-site agencies with a role to play in the intervention of a radiation emergency occurring at the premises. The local authority's own emergency response arrangements, dealing with the welfare of the population in the vicinity of the premises (including, for example, the provision of food and shelter), will be one of the detailed documents underpinning the off-site emergency plan. The off-site emergency plan covers all external agencies' activities, both those off-site and those helping with on-site mitigatory action. The operator's emergency plan would also refer to those external agencies providing on-site support; operator's and off-site emergency plans should dovetail.

208   Local authorities who must prepare emergency plans for the premises under other legislation, such as COMAH, may choose to prepare an integrated off-site emergency plan covering a range of radiation and chemical or other hazards. An effective off-site emergency plan could, therefore, satisfy the requirements of more than one set of regulations. An off-site emergency plan may also need to consider any adjacent or nearby REPPIR premises.

209   The principles which should be adopted for emergency planning for nuclear licensed sites regulated under NIA65 and other large fixed nuclear installations which have off-site emergency plans are as follows:

(a)   there should be a defined zone surrounding each installation (the detailed emergency planning zone) within which arrangements to protect the public are planned in detail. The boundary of the zone is defined in relation to the maximum size of any radiation emergency which can be reasonably foreseen;

(b) emergency planning needs to be capable of responding to radiation emergencies which, although extremely unlikely, could have consequences beyond the boundaries of the detailed emergency planning zone. The measures which are required cannot be precisely pre-planned because the nature and potential consequences of emergencies can vary, for example due to weather conditions, and the exact response must be based on an assessment made at the time. It is therefore important that emergency plans incorporate arrangements for 'extendibility' (see paragraph 138 in the 'Emergency plans' section).

210 Some of the requirements of REPPIR are already covered by existing nuclear site licence conditions under NIA65, including requirements for operator's (licensee's) emergency arrangements. Note that one aspect of REPPIR which is new and which may require changes to those arrangements is the provision for emergency exposures (see regulation 14). Nuclear site licence conditions requiring emergency arrangements are not replaced by REPPIR, but compliance with the conditions under NIA65 should satisfy equivalent provisions in REPPIR.

211 At nuclear licensed sites, under existing licence conditions, operators have a responsibility for ensuring emergency arrangements are in place; this is unchanged by REPPIR. However, a duty is now placed on local authorities to produce an off-site emergency plan. These requirements are not contradictory or mutually exclusive. The operator has an obligation to help with off-site mitigatory action (see regulation 7(2) and Schedule 7, Part I, paragraph (f)) similar to that of compliance with licence condition 11 for dealing with the effects of a radiation emergency.

212 In the case of off-site emergency plans relating to operators' emergency plans for berth or transit shed operators, there may be an overlap with emergency plans drawn up by harbour authorities or airport operators, respectively. Local authorities would need to take this into account. Also, the off-site emergency plan would need to take account of any adjacent or nearby REPPIR premises, and premises handling radioactive substances in quantities below the REPPIR thresholds (see guidance paragraph 296 on regulation 11(3)). (National contingency plans also exist for marine pollution from shipping and offshore installations.)

213 Off-site emergency plans prepared for nuclear powered vessels that form separate premises would cover the areas surrounding the relevant berths or fixed point moorings, including areas of estuaries, rivers or sea lochs in the vicinity of berths or moorings. Where such berths or fixed point moorings are at a nuclear licensed site or MoD controlled premises, then nuclear powered vessels are considered as part of that site or premises (see paragraph 44 on the definition of 'premises' in regulation 2(1)).

214 For all other premises where a radiation emergency is reasonably foreseeable, it is considered good practice for the principle of 'extendibility' to be part of the emergency planning arrangements. Adoption of this principle will ensure arrangements are in place to respond to situations where the emergency may be different to that predicted and additional measures may need to be taken. The arrangements will not be as detailed as those for the reasonably foreseeable event but will provide a framework for extending the response (see paragraph 138 in the 'Emergency plans' section).

215 The local authority's emergency plan should allow for the provision of possible reductions in staffing levels or closure of facilities during weekends, public holidays etc. This is to ensure the plan considers reasonably foreseeable situations when routine staffing levels may not be available.

**Regulation
9(2)**

(2) Without prejudice to paragraph (1), the off-site emergency plan shall contain the information specified in Part III of Schedule 7.

Guidance

9(2)

216 The local authority should ensure that the off-site emergency plan contains all the information required by Part III of Schedule 7.

217 The off-site emergency plan must establish the system for managing information in the event of a radiation emergency. This should ensure that necessary information can be identified and communicated to people off-site, the emergency services and other organisations identified in the plan as having a role to play and requiring information. Even where a radiation emergency has not yet resulted in off-site consequences, there are considerable benefits in keeping members of the public in the vicinity of the premises informed about what is happening. The local authority also has a duty to provide prior information and information in the event of a radiation emergency (see regulations 16 and 17).

**Regulation
9(3)**

(3) The off-site emergency plan prepared pursuant to paragraph (1) shall address each reasonably foreseeable radiation emergency that has been identified by the operator for the purposes of regulation 7(1).

Guidance

9(3)

218 The operator will advise the local authority on the possible consequences of any reasonably foreseeable radiation emergencies, so that the local authority can plan for such emergencies. The off-site emergency plan should cover any urgent early health protection countermeasures to be administered within the first 24 hours after a radiation emergency has occurred (eg the administration of 'stable iodine' tablets) in addition to addressing longer-term health protection recovery measures.

Regulation

9(4)

(4) Where an assessment has been made pursuant to regulation 4(1), within 28 days of sending the report of the assessment to the Executive in accordance with regulation 6(1), the operator shall supply to the local authority such information as is necessary for the purpose of enabling the authority to prepare the off-site emergency plan required by paragraph (1).

Guidance

9(4)

219 Local authorities do not have discretion under this regulation to accept information later than the 28-day deadline specified in the regulation. It is therefore most important that operators supply the necessary information within this timescale.

220 The local authority cannot prepare an off-site emergency plan for a premises without obtaining necessary information from the operator. The operator should ensure that any information supplied to the local authority is updated as necessary in the light of any changes that may take place.

Regulation

9(5)

(5) Without prejudice to paragraph (4), the operator shall further supply to the local authority -

(a) any additional information the local authority may reasonably request to enable the off-site emergency plan to be prepared; and

(b) details of any material change to the information provided under paragraph (4) resulting from -

(i) a further assessment made pursuant to regulation 5(1) or (2); or

(ii) a revision of the operator's emergency plan pursuant to regulation 10(1).

221 The local authority may ask the operator for additional information. The additional information requested must be relevant to the preparation of the off-site emergency plan. The information requested by the local authority should be provided as quickly as possible, with no unnecessary delays in the exchange of information.

222 If the review of the operator's hazard identification and risk evaluation assessment or the operator's emergency plan means that the information previously provided to the local authority is no longer appropriate, then the operator must provide the local authority with details of any material changes to that information.

(6) The information provided to a local authority pursuant to paragraphs (4) or (5)(a) shall be reviewed and where necessary revised by the operator at suitable intervals not exceeding 3 years from the date at which information was last supplied to the local authority under those paragraphs and the operator shall within 28 days inform the local authority of the outcome of that review.

223 The information provided by the operator before beginning work with ionising radiation, and any additional information requested by the local authority, must be reviewed at least every three years to see that the information is still appropriate. The operator must inform the local authority of the outcome of the review within 28 days of completing it, and let the local authority know either the details of changes to the information or that the information has not changed.

(7) The operator shall, within 28 days of any further assessment or revision referred to in paragraph (5)(b) inform the local authority of any material change to the information supplied arising from that assessment or review.

224 Following any further review of the operator's hazard identification and risk evaluation assessment or emergency plan, the operator must inform the local authority of details of changes to the information within 28 days of completing the review (see regulations 5(1) and 5(2) and 10(1)).

(8) Subject to paragraph (9), the off-site emergency plan shall be prepared no later than 6 months (or such longer period as the Executive may agree in writing) after whichever is the later of -

(a) the receipt by the local authority of a notice from the Executive informing the local authority of the need to prepare an off-site emergency plan in respect of the area; or

(b) the receipt by the local authority of the information referred to in paragraph (4).

225 The local authority must prepare the off-site emergency plan within six months of:

(a) being notified by the Executive that the local authority is required to prepare a plan; or

(b) receiving the information, from the operator, needed to prepare the plan under regulation 9(4).

226 If it seems unlikely that the off-site emergency plan would be completed within six months, then the local authority may ask HSE for an extension to complete the emergency plan. The request should explain why the delay has occurred, and HSE would consider the request. HSE may agree to a longer

Guidance
9(8)

Regulation
9(9)

Guidance
9(9)

Regulation
9(10)

Guidance

9(10)

Regulation
9(11)

Guidance

9(11)

period of time (than six months) for preparation of the off-site emergency plan, and would notify this extension in writing.

(9)   The off-site emergency plan shall be prepared before the operator carries out work with ionising radiation to which the assessment made in accordance with regulation 4(1) applies.

227   The local authority must prepare the off-site emergency plan and confirm its completion in writing, in accordance with regulation 9(13), before the operator can start working with ionising radiation (see regulation 7(3)(b)).

(10)   The off-site emergency plan shall be drawn up having regard to the principles set out in Part I of Schedule 8.

228   The off-site emergency plan must be drawn up taking account of the principles of intervention in Part I of Schedule 8. Intervention strategies will have to weigh up the benefits (advantages) of proposed intervention against the detriments (harm) of that intervention, and make sure that the benefits from intervention outweigh the detriments. Social costs (eg costs involved for the local population if they need to be evacuated) have to be taken into account as part of the detriment of intervention.

229   In REPPIR, emergency preparedness requires that provision be made to reduce the transfer of radioactive substances to people from the environment. Steps taken to protect human health may also provide much protection for the environment. Nevertheless, attention should be paid to the environmental harm which could result from a particular emergency intervention. Such harm would form part of the social cost and the detriment associated with the intervention, as referred to in sub-paragraphs (a) and (b) of Part I of Schedule 8. Remedial measures can affect the radioactive waste arising from a radiation emergency, and handling such waste may also contribute to costs to society.

230   In practice, the radiation protection aspects of the principles of intervention, regarding balancing the benefits and detriments of intervention, will already have been taken into account, because the operator should have already sought advice on radiation protection when compiling the information to give to the local authority to enable it to draw up the off-site emergency plan. Radiation protection advice can be sought from a range of sources including health authorities/boards.

231   Further guidance is available in the NEPLG consolidated guidance[15] and from NRPB (*Documents of the NRPB*, 1(4),[19] 5(1)[32] and 8(1)[20]) on emergency planning, emergency countermeasures, intervention regarding food and water, and recovery after a radiation emergency (see paragraphs 56-59 on the definition of 'radiation emergency' regarding health protection measures in regulation 2(1)).

(11)   Without prejudice to the generality of paragraph (1), the off-site emergency plan shall secure, where appropriate, intervention for the purposes set out in Part II of Schedule 8.

232   The off-site emergency plan must be drawn up taking account of the purposes of intervention in Part II of Schedule 8. The off-site agencies have a role to play in each of the purposes described:

(a)   the off-site agencies may have a role to play in reducing or stopping the release of radioactive substances from the premises. The off-site emergency plan should describe the measures and arrangements to do this as part of on-site mitigatory action;

(b) the off-site agencies have a key role in reducing the transfer of radioactive substances to individuals from the environment. The operator can advise on the quantities of radioactive substances released and the level and location of contamination off-site, so that those agencies can take steps to restrict the exposure of the public from radioactive substances in the environment. These steps may include, for example, advice on restrictions on the consumption of foodstuffs or water supplies. The off-site emergency plan should describe the arrangements to do this;

(c) the off-site emergency plan should describe arrangements to restrict the exposure of off-site intervention personnel when on the premises, and arrangements to restrict the exposure of intervention personnel and members of the public outside the premises (see guidance on emergency exposures for intervention personnel in regulation 14). These steps may include, for example, advice on sheltering or evacuation. The off-site emergency plan should describe arrangements to organise the effective medical treatment of people, and to receive advice from the operator on the nature of the radioactive substances released and on determining the level of exposure of people to ionising radiation, including personal contamination. The medical treatment is for both off- and on-site casualties, although it is most likely to be needed for on-site casualties.

233 As for the principles of intervention, in practice, the radiation protection aspects of the purposes of intervention will already have been taken into account, because the operator should have already sought advice on radiation protection when compiling the information to give to the local authority to enable it to draw up the off-site emergency plan.

9(11)

(12) For the purpose of preparing an off-site emergency plan pursuant to paragraph (1) or of reviewing the plan pursuant to regulation 10(1), the local authority shall consult -

(a) the operator carrying out the work with ionising radiation to which the plan relates, the Executive, the emergency services, each health authority in the vicinity of the premises of the operator and the Agency; and

(b) such other persons, bodies and authorities and members of the public as the local authority considers appropriate.

9(12)

234 The off-site emergency plan must dovetail with the operator's emergency plan, and the local authority will need to consult with the operator on the preparation of the off-site emergency plan.

235 The local authority should identify all the organisations that need to be consulted in the preparation of the off-site emergency plan. This will always include HSE, the operator, emergency services, health authority/board, and relevant Agency.

236 Local authorities must consult the emergency services on the preparation of the off-site emergency plan, so that their recommendations are taken into account in developing and resourcing the plan. The Home Office publication *Dealing with disaster* (Third Edition)[11] and Scottish Office (now Executive) *Dealing with disasters together*[12] contain guidelines for local authorities, emergency services, health authorities/boards and others. This highlights the importance of a combined response from all agencies involved, leading to

9(12)

integrated arrangements for emergency management. The emergency services must be consulted on the role that they would perform in the event of a radiation emergency, and discussions should include radiation protection arrangements for officers of the emergency services responding to such an emergency.

237   It will be necessary to consult with the appropriate health authorities/boards. Health authorities/boards have a responsibility to contribute to safeguarding the public health of the population within their geographical area. It is important for them to be aware of potential radiation emergencies so that they can dovetail their own emergency arrangements with those of the emergency services and the local authority. The health authorities/boards will themselves also consult (or facilitate consultation with) the appropriate hospital and emergency units and acute hospital trusts. Hospitals, accident and emergency departments and other trusts responsible for managing primary and community care within the vicinity of the premises need, wherever possible, to be aware in advance of the possibility of dealing with and treating large numbers of people or casualties requiring symptomatic or special treatment.

238   Each of the statutory consultees will need to consider whether they will need assistance from neighbouring authorities, for example local authorities, emergency services or health authorities/boards.

239   The local authority must consult the relevant Agency, in particular regarding the management, including disposal of radioactive waste arising from a radiation emergency; this would be EA for a local authority in England and Wales, or SEPA for a local authority in Scotland.

240   The local authority must also consult the public when preparing the off-site emergency plan. This could include:

(a)   consultation with elected councillors at county, borough and parish level (or equivalents); or

(b)   consultation with specially established groups representing residents in the vicinity of the site, for example local liaison committees.

241   Elected councillors will be able to use appropriate channels of communication with the public in the vicinity of the premises to obtain views on the developing emergency plan.

242   It may also be necessary to consult with other organisations who might be involved with or affected by implementation of the off-site emergency plan. Consultation should normally include certain Government departments, in particular: the Department for Environment, Food and Rural Affairs (DEFRA) in England; Scottish Executive Environment and Rural Affairs Department in Scotland; National Assembly for Wales, Agriculture Department in Wales); Food Standards Agency (FSA); DoH in England and Wales and SEHD in Scotland. Other organisations may include, for example, the water authority/supplier.

243   Local authorities should consult harbour authorities and airport operators, as appropriate, when preparing off-site emergency plans for berth or transit shed operators, as there may be an overlap between the off-site emergency planning zones and the areas covered by emergency plans prepared by harbour authorities or airport operators under DSHAR87 or CAP 168, respectively.

(13) Once it has prepared the off-site emergency plan the local authority shall confirm in writing to the operator that it has done so.

244 The local authority should inform the operator in writing, as soon as is practicable, that the off-site emergency plan has been completed.

(14) The employer of any employee who may be required to participate in the implementation of an off-site emergency plan shall ensure that such employees of his are or have been provided with -

(a) suitable and sufficient information, instruction and training; and

(b) the equipment necessary to restrict that employee's exposure to ionising radiation including, where appropriate, the issue of suitable dosemeters or other devices.

245 The purpose of regulation 9(14) is a general requirement for training and equipment for intervention personnel and for non-intervention personnel (eg headquarters staff). It applies whether or not emergency exposures are required (see guidance on regulations 14(1)(b), (c) and (g) regarding training and equipment when intervention personnel may receive emergency exposures).

246 Employees involved in intervention should be given appropriate training on how to fulfil their roles in the off-site emergency plan. Refresher training should be provided as appropriate. Arrangements should be in place to make sure that equipment necessary for intervention will be available during a radiation emergency, and that dosemeters (or other devices that may be used to determine radiation exposure) are also available (see guidance paragraphs 360-364 on regulation 14(1)(e) regarding obtaining dosemeters for this purpose).

247 All employers should make sure that all non-intervention personnel are given suitable and sufficient information and instruction on what to do in the event of a radiation emergency. This information may need to be repeated on an appropriate regular basis, and there should be arrangements in place to make sure that all employees new to the work are given information and instruction.

248 The operator would usually provide suitable and sufficient advice and assistance to all employers regarding training and equipment, including advice on radiation protection when considering the information, instruction and training given to employees, and the equipment and dosimetry provided for employees.

(15) The local authority shall provide to the Executive upon request and within such reasonable time as may be specified a copy of the off-site emergency plan or such parts of that plan as the Executive may require.

249 HSE may request a copy of the off-site emergency plan or parts of the plan. There is no need to routinely send a copy of the off-site emergency plan to HSE without being asked to do so.

Review and testing of emergency plans

(1) The operator, carrier or local authority who has prepared (or, in relation to a carrier, has ensured that there has been prepared) an emergency plan pursuant

to regulation 7, 8 or 9, as the case may be, shall at suitable intervals not exceeding 3 years -

(a) *review and where necessary revise the plan; and*

(b) *test the plan and take reasonable steps to arrange for the emergency services to participate in the test to such extent as is necessary,*

and any such review shall take into account changes occurring in the work with ionising radiation to which the plan relates and within the emergency services concerned, new technical knowledge and knowledge concerning the response to radiation emergencies and any material change to the assessment on which the plan was based since it was last reviewed or revised.

250 At least once every three years, the operator's emergency plan, carrier's emergency plan and off-site emergency plan must be both reviewed and tested. The first review and test must take place within three years of the first version of the emergency plan being completed. Operators of new sites who have prepared their assessment 12 months before operation may choose to review their operator's emergency plan at the same time that they review the assessment, that is within two years of operation, not three (see regulation 5(2) and paragraph 120). If any deficiencies are identified, the emergency plan must be revised. This is in addition to regular updates under safety management systems to reflect changes in the organisations to which they refer.

251 Changes which impact upon the operational effectiveness of the emergency plan must be incorporated as soon as possible, with subsequent distribution to all plan holders. Since the operator's emergency plan dovetails with the off-site emergency plan, each duty holder should inform the other of any changes made to the emergency plan which could have implications for the other plan.

Reviewing

252 Reviewing is a fundamental process, examining the adequacy and effectiveness of the components of the emergency plan and how they function together, including communication systems. The review process must take into account:

(a) all material changes to the assessments on which emergency plans are based;

(b) any changes in the emergency services relevant to the operation of emergency plans;

(c) advances in technical knowledge, for example new, more effective means of mitigation;

(d) changes in staffing resources including contractors;

(e) knowledge gained as a result of radiation emergencies occurring, either on-site or elsewhere; and

(f) lessons learned during the testing of emergency plans.

253 For this to take place effectively there has to be open communication between the operator or carrier and the local authority, emergency services

and other relevant external agencies. All appropriate changes which may affect the emergency response should be communicated to the other parties.

254 A review of the adequacy and accuracy of the emergency planning arrangements should follow any significant changes (such as changes in radionuclides used, plant modifications, or organisational structure). Under these circumstances, operators or carriers should not wait until the three-year review is due to review their emergency plans.

255 There is a need to ensure the lessons learned are shared/distributed to appropriate organisations, for example NEPLG (Lessons Learned Sub-Group), Cabinet Office, LGA and COSLA.

Testing

256 An emergency plan test is a task or tasks undertaken to give confidence in the accuracy, completeness, practicability and adequacy of the plan. It should test:

(a) the completeness, consistency and accuracy of the emergency plan and other documentation used by organisations responding to an emergency;

(b) the adequacy of the equipment and facilities and their operability, especially under emergency conditions; and

(c) the competence of staff to carry out the duties identified for them in the emergency plan, and their use of the equipment and facilities.

257 Testing should be able to demonstrate that intervention personnel following the emergency plan could deal adequately with the range of reasonably foreseeable radiation emergencies that could occur. It should give an indication of the conditions that may exist on and off the premises, or during a rail transport incident. It should also show that the plan would work as proposed to control and mitigate the effects of an emergency, and to communicate necessary information to all involved.

258 Testing an emergency plan may consist of a live exercise, or a table-top exercise supported by the testing of other components (which may be done at separate times) including the communication arrangements. Testing must be carried out at least once every three years. Testing will usually examine the response during the emergency phase, and may examine aspects of the recovery phase where appropriate. If table-top exercises are carried out there is a need to ensure that the constituent parts of the plan, including the emergency response arrangements of different organisations, will work together. The testing of other components should demonstrate whether the plan can be put into effect successfully. The testing of some of the components should be done live, ie it should involve deployment of some personnel and resources as if they were responding to a real emergency.

259 Media arrangements should be tested where these are included in an emergency plan. This should involve appropriate responding organisations and their staff delegated to manage media relations (for further guidance on the media, see 'Emergency plans' section and the NEPLG consolidated guidance document[15] regarding media briefing centres for use in the event of a civil nuclear emergency).

260 Information technology or virtual reality systems are being developed to simulate accidents which enable emergency responders to develop their skills

and responses to them. Under some circumstances, such systems may be useful when carrying out table-top and 'control post' communication exercises.

261 The scenario should vary in each three-year cycle to test over time the range of emergency responses required for the range of reasonably foreseeable radiation emergencies which might arise. Extended arrangements should also be tested (see paragraph 138 of the 'Emergency plans' section and guidance paragraph 305 to regulation 12 regarding the off-site emergency plan).

262 All relevant staff in all shifts in all the relevant organisations should be fully trained in their expected response in the event of a radiation emergency. A test of an emergency plan is not a training exercise, although there may be training benefits. Emergency plan testing required under REPPIR is to demonstrate that the plans are accurate, complete, practicable and adequate.

263 There are considerable benefits to be gained from testing the operator's and off-site emergency plans (or parts of plans) at the same time. These benefits include ensuring that both emergency plans work effectively together and offering potential financial savings by avoiding duplicate testing. For example, the external agencies' roles in mitigation, both on and off the site, are described only in the off-site emergency plan (not in the operator's emergency plan). Exercising this part of the off-site emergency plan with the operator's emergency plan can test effective co-ordination of all emergency response personnel handling a radiation emergency on the site.

264 Before the test is undertaken, agreement should be reached between the operator or carrier and the emergency services and local authority on the scale and nature of the emergency plan test (there will be individual agency objectives as well as over-arching combined response objectives for the test).

265 Clarifying objectives is assisted by the agreement by all participants of what is to be tested - a particular component part or the 'complete' emergency plan - and what resources are required to demonstrate the adequacy of the plan. Where possible, a reasonably accurate estimate of the cost of the proposed testing regime should be made, and the aspects of the test for which charges can be made should be agreed (see regulation 12).

266 Some of the requirements in REPPIR are already covered by existing nuclear site licence conditions, including requirements relating to testing emergency plans (covered by exercising emergency arrangements). Emergency exercises under nuclear site licence conditions should satisfy the equivalent requirements of REPPIR. The response to a real emergency by the operator, carrier, emergency services and other organisations is not considered to be a suitable or adequate substitute for the testing of an emergency plan.

267 For further guidance on testing, see the NEPLG consolidated guidance document. This includes testing facilities, equipment and communication links between emergency centres, the need for occasional live exercises, and a revised approach to testing off-site nuclear emergency plans; this guidance is also relevant to non-nuclear premises.

Evaluation of testing

268 For organisations to get the most out of their participation in emergency plan tests, it is important to evaluate the lessons learned to determine whether modifications are required to the plan and to promote good practice. With many organisations being involved, there will not be one single method for evaluating the effectiveness of the plan test, and each organisation may want to

establish its own self-evaluation criteria relevant to its own response. However, there should be consistency of approach for evaluating the effectiveness of the interfaces between responding organisations. For example, organisations may want to set quantitative measures for timeliness of response, or qualitative measures for effective performance.

269   Ideally, the debriefing following an emergency plan exercise should be carried out in an open and blame-free atmosphere. This should allow any issues on implementing the emergency plan to be identified, the reasons for the problems to be discussed and appropriate solutions to be considered, so appropriate improvements can be identified. In the aftermath of a radiation emergency or an incident which had the potential to become a radiation emergency, such open discussion and consideration may be difficult to achieve.

Training

270   Training should be kept as up to date as appropriate, and be supplemented with suitable refresher training as necessary. All those involved in testing should have had previous training for their role in the emergency response (even if this is only to follow instructions).

271   All relevant staff in all shifts in all the relevant organisations should be fully trained in their expected response in the event of a radiation emergency. As staff change (turnover, reallocation of duties etc) training or retraining should be provided by the employer (see training requirements in regulations 7(7), 8(8), 9(14) and 14(1)(b) and (g)).

Operator's emergency plan

272   Operators are required to test their emergency plans at their site at least once every three years. Operators of premises with a number of radiation sources in different installations with the potential to cause a reasonably foreseeable radiation emergency should consider testing the emergency arrangements for each such installation at least once during the three-year cycle. On some premises there will be scope for economies of scale, using lessons learned from live exercises on some installations, supported by appropriate table-top exercises for other installations. This will depend upon similarities in the hazards and risks posed, and on the type of emergency response. There is also the option to test the operator's and off-site emergency plans together.

273   It is important that the lessons learned from such joint exercises are fed back to all relevant managers, supervisors and employees at the relevant installations on the premises. Conclusions should be drawn from the findings of the test in relation to all installations under examination.

274   Berth or transit shed operators may decide to test aspects of their emergency plans at the same time as local authorities test the off-site emergency plans, or harbour authorities or airport operators test their own emergency arrangements under other legislation (eg DSHAR87). There would be benefits to all parties in this, as the way in which the various plans dovetail together could be assessed.

275   Dealing with the on-site consequences of radiation emergencies will usually require the assistance of the emergency services such as the fire service and, therefore, it may be appropriate for them to attend many of the tests, but not necessarily all.

Carrier's emergency plan

276 Carriers are required to test their emergency plans at least once every three years. The carrier will have to choose a location to test the emergency plan, and then gain the co-operation of the local authority and emergency services for that location to participate in testing the plan. The carrier may choose to involve the consignor in these discussions. Where the local authority or emergency services attend a test at the request of the carrier, they can charge for their attendance (see regulation 12). This need not necessarily involve a full-scale live exercise. Testing could consist of examining the principal components of the plan as it applies at the location chosen for the test. Two distinct approaches to testing these components are:

(a) 'control post' communication exercises to examine the adequacy of the communication arrangements between all the players during a radiation emergency; and

(b) table-top exercises, based on a suitable scenario or scenarios identified in the hazard identification and risk evaluation assessment report, to examine the command and control arrangements and inter-agency liaison during an emergency.

277 Testing in this way should be co-ordinated and agreed locally to give the maximum benefit to all the players. The two components (ie the communication arrangements and the command and control arrangements) must be examined at least once over the three-year period. There will be considerable benefits from carrying out some of the exercises, for example the 'control post' communication exercise (as it applies to different parts of the carrier's organisation), more frequently. It is important that the lessons learned from such exercises are fed back to all relevant managers, supervisors and employees, and also fed into any review of the carrier's plan, either under REPPIR or as part of a review under RSCR, regulation 6.

278 RSCR requires carriers (train operators) to provide 'particulars' of their arrangements for handling emergencies in their safety case. The HM Railway Inspectorate Assessment Criteria[28] state that a description of what the operator does to review and test the plan is an example of evidence that satisfies this requirement to provide 'particulars', but reviewing and testing are not in themselves duties under RSCR. Thus, as in REPPIR, RSCR places the duty to provide particulars on the carrier, instead of the consignor. However, it is important that the consignor or their agents (with the appropriate specialist expertise) support these emergency arrangements in both REPPIR and RSCR. This is particularly important as far as the consignor is concerned as the carrier's response arrangements are similar for all types of rail accident - it is the specialist support provided by the consignor that is different with incidents or accidents of this nature. This means that there is a particular value in exercising the response capability of the consignor as part of any test of the carrier's emergency plan under REPPIR. The carrier may choose to carry out a test that also satisfies HM Railway Inspectorate's Assessment Criteria.

Off-site emergency plan

279 Local authorities are required to test their off-site emergency plans at least once every three years. This need not necessarily involve a full-scale live exercise. Testing could consist of examining the principal component parts of the emergency plan. These would include:

(a) site visits by all off-site agencies with an on-site role to play in the emergency response, for familiarisation;

55

(b) 'control post' communication exercises to examine the adequacy of the communication arrangements between all the key players during a radiation emergency; and

(c) table-top exercises based on a suitable scenario or scenarios identified in the hazard identification and risk evaluation assessment report, to examine the command and control arrangements and inter-agency liaison during an emergency.

280 Testing in this way should be co-ordinated and agreed locally to give the maximum benefit to local authorities, operators and emergency services. There will be considerable benefits from carrying out some of the exercises, for example the site familiarisation visits and the 'control post' communication exercise, more frequently. It is important to ensure all components of the emergency plan are tested during the three-year period.

281 In some local authority areas, there may be scope for economies of scale within the testing regime. It may be possible for one live or table-top exercise to test the off-site emergency plan for two or more premises (eg adjacent premises). This will depend upon the similarities of their location and of the hazards and risks posed to the nearby population. Each operator would have to test the site-specific features of their own premises in some other way, for example as part of the operator's emergency plan test or the 'control post' communication exercise. There is also the option to test the operator's and off-site emergency plans together. For further guidance on testing off-site emergency plans for nuclear licensed sites, see the chapter on testing emergency plans in the NEPLG consolidated guidance document.

282 It is important that the lessons learned from such joint tests are fed back to all the relevant operators, emergency services and organisations. Conclusions should be drawn from the findings of the test in relation to all the premises under examination.

283 Local authorities may decide to test their off-site emergency arrangements for ports and airports under DSHAR87 or COMAH at the same time as their off-site emergency plans for berth or transit shed operators under REPPIR. There would be benefits to all parties in this, as the way in which the various plans dovetail together could be assessed.

Revision

284 Review and revision of emergency plans must be undertaken at least once every three years. Review and revision are different from updating emergency plans. Updating plans is an on-going process which is carried out to reflect any changes in the practical details of the emergency response arrangements, for example changes in the responding organisations' communication arrangements or the mitigation equipment to be mobilised. Emergency plans include names or positions. When names are used when referring to personnel, however, updating should include changing the names whenever personnel changes occur, rather than waiting for the three yearly review of plans. It is recommended that the names and telephone numbers of authorised personnel are included in the annexes of emergency plans; this will help with updating.

285 To obtain the maximum benefit from testing emergency plans it is important to evaluate the lessons learned from the tests, to determine where modifications are required to the emergency plans, and to promote good practice. One of the principal inputs to the process of reviewing and revising emergency plans will come, therefore, from the results of tests of the

emergency plans. After the test, the review should concentrate on areas where the objectives were not met. Recommendations from reviews and tests of emergency plans should be logged, along with actions taken to address each recommendation; this should happen as soon as possible. Amendments to the emergency plan can then be followed up to ensure that all the lessons learned from testing have led to improvements which can be traced through an audit trail. Information to the public should also be updated via the operator, carrier or local authority if necessary (see regulation 16).

(2)   The local authority shall endeavour to reach agreement with the operator who is subject to a duty to prepare an operator's emergency plan and the emergency services as to how the off-site emergency plan is to be tested.

286   The local authority, operator and emergency services will need to agree the overall objectives of the testing required by regulation 10(1), and the best way of meeting those objectives. This may take account of other tests being carried out at the premises or in the vicinity. A suitable scenario or scenarios will have to be developed from the hazard identification and risk evaluation assessment report, and the type and nature of the test agreed. It will be necessary to identify which organisations are to participate in the test and for each of these organisations to determine their own objectives, which should be consistent with the overall objectives of the test.

287   If the local authority wishes to test the berth or transit shed operator's off-site emergency plan in conjunction with its other emergency plans for the harbour or airport, the local authority will have to endeavour to reach agreement with all the various parties on how the test should be carried out and how any costs should be apportioned (see guidance paragraph 304 on regulation 12).

288   If the local authority cannot reach agreement with the operator and the emergency services, regulation 10(1) still requires the local authority to test the off-site emergency plan at a suitable interval not exceeding three years.

(3)   The carrier shall endeavour to reach agreement with such local authorities and emergency services as are appropriate as to how the carrier's emergency plan is to be tested.

289   Having chosen a location in which to test the carrier's emergency plan, and having gained the co-operation of the local authority and the emergency services in that location to participate in testing that emergency plan, the carrier must attempt to reach agreement on how that emergency plan is to be tested with both the local authority and the emergency services. The carrier may choose to involve the consignor in these discussions.

290   The carrier will need to agree with the local authority and the emergency services the overall objectives of the test of its emergency plan and the most appropriate way to achieve those objectives. This may take account of other tests being carried out by the carrier at other locations. A suitable scenario or scenarios will have to be developed from the hazard identification and risk evaluation assessment report, and the type and nature of the test agreed. It will be necessary to identify which organisations are to participate in the test and for each of these organisations to determine their own objectives, which should be consistent with the overall objectives of the test.

291   If the carrier cannot reach agreement with the local authority and the emergency services, regulation 10(1) still requires the carrier to test the carrier's emergency plan at a suitable interval not exceeding three years. (The carrier may decide to test the emergency plan at a different location.)

Consultation and co-operation

(1) In performing the duties imposed on him by regulations 4(1)(a), 4(2), 5 and 7, the operator shall consult any other employer who carries out work with ionising radiation on the premises and shall for the purpose of compliance with those duties take into account relevant matters arising from that consultation.

(2) Any employer who carries out work with ionising radiation at premises to which these Regulations apply shall co-operate with the operator by providing information or otherwise to the extent necessary to ensure that the operator is enabled to comply with the requirements of these Regulations (including the testing of emergency plans) in so far as his ability depends on such co-operation.

292   There may be a number of employers working with ionising radiation (called 'radiation employers' in the 1999 Regulations) on a single premises (see guidance paragraphs 36-45 on the definition of 'premises' in regulation 2(1)). In such a case, if the total quantities of radioactive substances on the premises exceed the REPPIR thresholds, the operator of that premises must undertake an assessment (see regulation 4(1)(a)) and prepare an emergency plan (see regulation 7) which takes account of all employers' radioactive substances on the premises. This requires the operator to consult and each (radiation) employer to co-operate as necessary during this process. They must also work together when reviewing and testing the assessment and emergency plan, respectively.

(3) Any person who is subject to a duty under these Regulations to prepare an emergency plan and any employer of any other person whose participation is reasonably required by any such plan shall co-operate with each other by the exchange of information or otherwise to the extent necessary to ensure that each person is enabled to comply with the requirements of these Regulations (including the testing of emergency plans) in so far as his ability to comply depends upon such co-operation.

293   Emergency preparedness involves many separate organisations, and for mitigation to be effective, all parties concerned must work together. Regulation 11(3) helps to achieve effective mitigation by requiring duty holders who have prepared emergency plans (namely the operator, carrier and local authority) and employers of other intervention personnel (particularly the emergency services) to co-operate. Any person who has a role within emergency plans also must co-operate with others, and this includes organisations such as health authorities/boards. This co-operation may be by exchanging information or by other means, and should be to the extent necessary to enable the duty holders to fulfil their duties under REPPIR, in so far as their ability to do so depends on such co-operation.

294   Regulations 7(6), 8(7) and 9(12), in addition to 11(1), specify particular duties of consultation in the preparation of emergency plans. One purpose of consultation and co-operation provides a framework for ensuring that provision of training and equipment for all intervention personnel is co-ordinated. Through this co-operation, discussions between key stakeholders can take place. For example, the local authority will need to draw on the technical expertise of the operator or carrier (or consignor) and their radiation protection specialist, and this can inform discussions on emergency exposures for employees of the emergency services.

295   For premises, the duty to co-operate on emergency plans includes the co-operation of the operators to provide the emergency services with necessary information to enable then to perform their functions, which would be described in the off-site emergency plan.

296 If there is more than one berth or transit shed handling REPPIR quantities of radionuclides at the same port or airport, the operators should co-operate with each other. Similarly, these berth or transit shed operators should co-operate with any rail carriers involved with inward or onward transport of radioactive substances by rail where the carrier is using railway sidings which form part of an installation on their premises. DSHAR87 requires berth operators, if requested, to co-operate with harbour authorities on preparing their emergency plans. Such co-operation is particularly important in view of the potential risks from radioactive substances being transported, transferred or conveyed within the port which may have implications for adjacent employers handling quantities of radioactive substances below REPPIR thresholds.

Regulation 12

Charge for preparation, review and testing of emergency plans

Regulation

12(1)-(3)

(1)   A local authority may charge -

(a)   the operator a fee for performing the local authority's functions in relation to the off-site emergency plan under regulations 9 and 10; and

(b)   the carrier a fee for performing the local authority's functions in relation to the carrier's emergency plan under regulation 10(1)(b).

(2)   The fee charged under paragraph (1) shall not exceed the sum of costs reasonably incurred by the local authority in performing the functions referred to in that paragraph, including (but without prejudice to the generality of the foregoing provision of this paragraph) any costs reasonably incurred by the local authority in arranging for the emergency services to participate in the testing of the off-site emergency plan or the carrier's plan, as the case may be.

(3)   When requiring payment the local authority shall send or give to the operator or carrier, as the case may be, a detailed statement of the work done and the costs incurred including the dates of any site visits and the period to which the statement relates and the fee, which shall be recoverable only as a civil debt, shall become payable one month after the statement has been sent or given.

Guidance

12(1)-(3)

Estimating costs in advance

297 Where possible, a reasonably accurate estimate of the cost of the proposed testing regime should be made, and the aspects of the test for which charges can be made should be agreed (see regulation 10).

298 The agreement of resources required for the test identifies the chargeable activities. If one or more agencies then chooses to bring in extra resources, for additional training purposes, these would be non-chargeable activities as they would be beyond the requirements of the demonstration of the adequacy of the emergency plan. For example, if a test requires one fire appliance to attend the incident, but the fire service wished to include a second appliance for additional training purposes, the operator or carrier should only be charged for the participation of one appliance.

299 The system for recording the work done by the local authority to enable their costs to be recovered should be agreed with the operator or carrier before starting the work. The system should be transparent but should not overburden local authority staff.

Off-site emergency plan

300 The local authority may charge the operator for its costs in preparing, reviewing, revising and testing the off-site emergency plan plus any costs incurred by the emergency services in testing the off-site emergency plan (which includes on-site mitigatory action). Where emergency services attend an operator's test at the request of the operator, they can charge for their attendance under arrangements for providing assistance with on-site mitigatory action as part of testing the off-site emergency plan. The operator cannot be charged for the emergency services' involvement in the preparation, review and revision of the off-site emergency plan.

301 The charges can only cover costs that have been reasonably incurred. Where the work is carried out by local authority staff, the charge should be based on the time spent by officers of the appropriate grades including the average costs of their employment overheads (ie full cost). Where emergency services help the local authority to test the off-site emergency plan, their costs should also be based on the full costs of time spent.

302 A local authority may decide to contract out some of the work to another organisation, in which case the authority may recover the costs of the contract from the operator, but these would still have to be reasonable.

303 The economies of scale permitted in the regime for testing off-site emergency plans should reduce the burden on all operators whose plans are under examination. For example, if a live exercise is carried out at one premises to test the off-site emergency plan of three premises (eg adjacent transit sheds), then the operators of all three premises should contribute as appropriate to cover the charge made by the local authority. The operators of the two premises where the test is not carried out may have to carry out additional exercises to address premises-specific aspects of their off-site emergency plans. They will have to cover any charges associated with these premises-specific exercises.

304 If there is a combined test of either a berth operator's off-site emergency plan and the harbour authority's emergency plan under DSHAR87, or a transit shed operator's emergency plan and the airport operator's emergency arrangements under CAP 168, then the local authority should agree to an apportioning of costs to the berth or transit shed operator in advance.

305 The charges that local authorities make for testing off-site emergency plans, including the costs incurred by emergency services, should only cover costs of testing to make sure that emergency plans are accurate, complete and practical. If the test is made broader than this for other reasons, such as to provide training opportunities, then charges should not be extended to cover the additional costs. So, emergency services can only charge for the level of input required by the local authority and not for any extra resource devoted because of the resulting training benefit. Similarly, if the test is broadened to cover extended arrangements, then costs should not be extended to cover the additional costs (see paragraph 138 in the 'Emergency plans' section and guidance paragraph 261 on regulation 10(1) regarding testing).

306 In presenting a charge to the operator, the local authority should provide an itemised, detailed statement of work done and costs incurred. Any dispute arising over the charge is a matter for resolution by the parties concerned, if necessary through the civil courts.

Carrier's emergency plan

307 The local authority may recover its costs from the carrier in testing the carrier's emergency plan plus any costs incurred by the emergency services in testing the plan. Cost recovery is not available for tests of carrier's emergency plans which are outside the scope of REPPIR, for example exclusive testing of Type B package scenarios (exempt from REPPIR).

308 The charges can only cover costs that have been reasonably incurred. Where the work is carried out by local authority staff, the charge should be based on the time spent by officers of the appropriate grades including the average costs of their employment overheads.

309 A local authority may decide to contract out some of the work to another organisation, in which case the local authority may recover the costs of the contract from the carrier, but these would still have to be reasonable.

310 In principle, economies of scale for testing operators' emergency plans are also applicable to testing carriers' emergency plans, but in practice there may be little benefit to rail transport.

311 Before testing is carried out, agreement should be reached between carriers, the host local authority and emergency services on the scale and nature of testing, and a reasonably accurate estimate of the cost of the proposed testing schedule should be made.

312 The charges that local authorities make for testing carrier's emergency plans, including the costs incurred by emergency services, should only cover costs of testing to make sure that emergency plans are accurate, complete and practical. If the test is made broader than this for other reasons, such as to provide training opportunities, then charges should not be extended to cover the additional costs.

313 In presenting a charge to the carrier, the local authority should provide an itemised, detailed statement of work done and costs incurred. Any dispute arising over the charge is a matter for resolution by the parties concerned, if necessary through the civil courts.

Implementation of emergency plans

314 A radiation emergency begins when an emergency plan is implemented to deal with an event which leads to (or is likely to lead to) a member of the public receiving a dose of ionising radiation above the levels specified in Schedule 1. Delays in implementing emergency plans should be minimised, and discussions to minimise delays should take place with all statutory consultees in the preparation of the emergency plan.

315 The duty to implement the operator's, carrier's and off-site emergency plans lies with the operator, carrier and the local authority, respectively, not on actual individuals who draw up the plans. The operator, carrier or local authority will have discharged this duty when there are systems in place to ensure there are no unreasonable delays between the discovery of an event which leads to (or is likely to lead to) a member of the public receiving a dose of ionising radiation above the levels specified in Schedule 1, and activation of the operator's, carrier's or off-site emergency plan.

61

316   There should be a clear and logical decision-making system in place to ensure that, as soon as a relevant event has occurred, the appropriate emergency plan will be initiated. This should include arrangements for the operator or carrier to notify the emergency services, local authority, health authority/board, relevant Agency and other organisations of an event which may escalate into a radiation emergency. These arrangements should be described in the emergency plans (see Schedule 7, Parts I and II).

317   A phased approach to the implementation of emergency plans could be adopted for premises. Initially, the operator's emergency plan could be activated when a relevant event occurs (or one which could reasonably be expected to lead to a radiation emergency). At this stage the off-site emergency plan is put on alert (stand-by) but not necessarily implemented, with emergency responders advised of a potential situation. At this point notification may not have been given to the general public as the off-site plan has not been implemented. However, there may be advantages to keeping members of the public informed (see guidance to regulation 7(2)). The off-site plan could be activated as a precautionary approach with the operator's emergency plan if it is possible the incident will escalate.

318   In an escalating situation, the off-site emergency plan would be implemented. If the situation does not develop or is contained, remaining an on-site incident only, the off-site emergency plan may not be implemented at all. However, while the operator's emergency plan can be implemented without the off-site plan, in practice this may be rare, as the on-site mitigatory assistance of external agencies is within the off-site emergency plan.

319   The person or persons shown in the emergency plan as having responsibility for initiating the plan should do so in accordance with the plan. The emergency services should be alerted in accordance with the plan to ensure that no unnecessary delays occur, as these could have serious consequences.

320   The emergency plans will explain roles and responsibilities (see Schedule 7). The duty to implement the plan remains with the operator, carrier or local authority, although, by agreement (and the procedure written into the appropriate emergency plan) someone acting on their behalf, for example the police or fire service, may initiate the emergency plan. Organisations should implement their own emergency arrangements when an appropriate warning is received.

(1)   An operator or carrier who has prepared (or, in relation to a carrier, has ensured that there has been prepared) an emergency plan pursuant to regulation 7 or 8, as the case may be, shall take reasonable steps to put it, or such parts of it as are necessary, into effect without delay when -

(a)   a radiation emergency occurs, or

(b)   an event occurs which could reasonably be expected to lead to a radiation emergency,

and shall notify such occurrence to the Executive without delay.

321   For premises, if there is an alarm/siren system as part of the arrangements, there needs to be agreement as to who will initiate any alarm/siren and this should be documented in the emergency plan (see guidance on regulation 17, regarding supplying information in the event of a radiation emergency). It could be appropriate for an employee of the operator of a premises to be identified (by name or position) in the emergency plan as

having the responsibility for sounding any off-site alarm/siren. Alternatively, sounding an off-site alarm/siren could be the responsibility of an external organisation (see guidance paragraphs 324-325 on regulation 13(2)).

322 Some of the requirements of REPPIR are already covered by existing nuclear site licence conditions under NIA65 (eg the licensee implementing the emergency plan is covered by the emergency arrangements). For a nuclear licensed site regulated under NIA65, these requirements should be met by the requirements of the nuclear site licence. REPPIR will not replace existing nuclear site licence conditions but compliance with the conditions should satisfy equivalent provisions in REPPIR (licence condition 11).

323 For rail transport, the Transport of Dangerous Goods (Safety Advisers) Regulations 1999[33] place a responsibility on the Adviser to monitor the implementation of proper emergency procedures in the event of an accident or incident that may affect safety during the transport of dangerous goods. The operator or carrier should seek advice on radiation protection as necessary when implementing the emergency plan (or, in the case of the carrier, ensure that this is done).

(2) A local authority which has prepared an emergency plan pursuant to regulation 9 shall take reasonable steps to ensure that it, or such parts of it as are necessary, is put into effect without delay when informed by the operator that -

(a) a radiation emergency has occurred; or

(b) an event has occurred which could reasonably be expected to lead to a radiation emergency.

324 As soon as the operator (or a body acting on the operator's behalf, such as the police service) has informed the responding organisations that a radiation emergency or an event that may lead to a radiation emergency has occurred, the off-site emergency plan must be implemented without delay in accordance with the agreed arrangements, following a clear and logical decision-making system.

325 The persons specified in the off-site emergency plan as being authorised to initiate the plan should take action without delay to do so. The persons responsible for sounding any off-site siren/alarm or other warning systems to alert the public of a radiation emergency should also take appropriate action (see guidance to regulation 13(1)). Organisations should implement their own emergency arrangements when an appropriate warning is received.

(3) In the event of a radiation emergency resulting from his work with ionising radiation, the operator or carrier shall -

(a) as soon as is reasonably practicable, make (or, in relation to a carrier, ensure that there has been made) a provisional assessment of the circumstances and consequences of such an emergency and for this purpose shall consult -

(i) in the case of the operator, the emergency services, the local authority, the health authority, the Agency and such other persons, bodies or authorities as have functions under the operator's emergency plan or the off-site emergency plan; and

(ii) in the case of the carrier, the consignor, the Agency and any emergency services, local authority and health authority who were involved in the response to the emergency and such other persons, bodies or authorities as have functions under the carrier's emergency plan;

Guidance

326 In the event of a radiation emergency, the priority will be to manage the emergency phase of the incident to ensure effective mitigation. During the initial stages, radiological data and events occurring will inform decisions on actions to be taken and countermeasures to be instigated. Records should be kept of radiological data, events occurring, decisions taken and actions carried out, as appropriate.

327 As soon as is reasonably practicable, a provisional assessment can be made of the circumstances that led to the release of radioactive material, and the circumstances that contributed to stopping that release. The records of radiological data etc will inform the provisional assessment. This should also include an initial assessment (or estimation) of doses received by people, and the likely effect on the environment which may affect people, such as implications for foodstuffs and drinking water. This will inform decisions on how to maintain the integrity of the source, and how to move forward into the recovery phase.

328 Depending on the nature of the radiation emergency, the incident may be moving into the recovery phase before the provisional assessment can be completed. Data necessary for the provisional assessment may include data from personal dosimetry, *in vivo* monitoring, workplace monitoring and environmental sampling. Information necessary for the provisional assessment may include an analysis of the structural integrity of the plant, and an evaluation of the success of the countermeasures taken.

329 This provisional assessment should be made by the operator if the radiation emergency began on the premises, and by the carrier if the radiation emergency resulted from a transport incident.

330 When making the provisional assessment, the operator must consult with all organisations having a role to play in the operator's and off-site emergency plans. Similarly, the carrier must consult with all organisations having a role to play in the carrier's emergency plan, and with all those who were directly involved in the intervention. In addition, the carrier may need to seek the technical expertise of the consignors of the radioactive substances being transported.

13(3)

Regulation

13(3)

(b) *as soon as is practicable and in any event within 12 months or such longer time as the Executive may agree, make (or in relation to a carrier ensure that there has been made) a full assessment of the consequences of that emergency and the effectiveness of the emergency plans put into effect as a result of that emergency; and*

Guidance

331 The full implications of the radiation emergency may not be known for some time following the event. Dose assessments of internal radiation from long-lived radionuclides, such as actinides, may take many months to complete. The impact of contamination on crops, animals and fish, and their effects on the food chain may continue for many months. The impact of radioactive waste arising from the radiation emergency may also need to be assessed. Therefore the time within which a full assessment of the radiation emergency can be made will depend on the nature of the emergency.

332 The operator or carrier must complete their full assessment as soon as practicable, and in any event within one year of the radiation emergency occurring. If a longer period of time is necessary to complete the assessment, then this must be agreed with HSE.

13(3)

(c)   within 28 days of the completion of the assessment under sub-paragraph (b) make a report of the findings of the assessment and retain that report or a copy thereof for at least 50 years from the date upon which the report was completed.

333   The report (or a copy) of the full assessment must be kept for at least 50 years, which is also the period of time that reports of certain occurrences involving releases of radioactive substances must be retained in the 1999 Regulations.

(4)   The operator or carrier shall provide to the Executive within 28 days of the making of the report under paragraph (3)(c) above a copy of that report.

334   A copy of the full assessment must be sent to HSE within 28 days of completing the report.

Regulation 14

Emergency exposures

335   Emergency exposures, defined in regulation 2(1), are exposures to ionising radiation of intervention personnel which may be necessary to put emergency plans into effect. The operator or carrier should seek advice on radiation protection regarding all matters relating to emergency exposures, including training of employees, provision of equipment, provision of dosimetry and medical surveillance, and evaluation of dose levels. The operator or carrier should also provide advice on radiation protection to employers of other intervention personnel, such as the emergency services, although the carrier is likely to seek such advice from a consignor.

336   Regulation 14 is **not** concerned with doses received by employees who may be exposed to ionising radiation as a direct result of the radiation accident that leads to the radiation emergency. Such doses are subject to the requirements for accident doses in regulation 23 of the 1999 Regulations. Only the doses received by employees who are involved in the response to the radiation emergency are the subject of this regulation.

337   Not all radiation emergencies will involve emergency exposures, indeed it is likely that most radiation emergencies can be managed without recourse to emergency exposures for intervention personnel. Decisions about the need for emergency exposures of employees in radiation emergency situations and the emergency dose levels that should apply are an integral part of emergency plan development. It is therefore important that operators and carriers address these issues in an integrated way so that emergency exposure and dose level decision-making informs the process of intervention strategy development rather than becoming a last resort course of action in radiation emergency management.

338   The provisions of regulation 14 only apply for those radiation emergencies where a risk evaluation has identified the possibility that doses to intervention personnel in excess of the dose limits in the 1999 Regulations for employees aged over 18 years of age could be incurred, and where appropriate provision has been made in the emergency plan.

339   It is envisaged that emergency exposures may be required for intervention personnel on-site in the event of a radiation emergency. Arrangements for emergency exposures for people working on-site would be covered in the operator's emergency plan, and arrangements for external intervention personnel coming on to the premises (particularly members of the

fire service) would be covered in the off-site emergency plan. It is much less likely that they would be required for personnel working off-site, but this possibility is not excluded by the Regulations. Thus, if the off-site emergency plan includes arrangements for such emergency exposures, the provisions of this regulation will apply, and arrangements for the management of those exposures for off-site personnel will be necessary.

340   In the event of a radiation emergency, it is vital to have expert advice on radiation protection available to help manage emergency exposures. Arranging for expert(s) to be available should form part of the emergency plans. Such experts may be radiation protection advisers (RPAs) under the 1999 Regulations, or they may be other individuals with appropriate qualifications and experience. Emergency services should be able to turn to operators or carriers as appropriate to obtain the expert advice they would need although the carrier is likely to seek such advice from a consignor.

341   This regulation provides a management framework for controlling the exposure of intervention personnel. Its purpose is to ensure that the need for emergency exposures is recognised in advance, and preparations are made to manage the exposures and keep them as low as is reasonably practicable. The elements of this framework are as follows:

(a)   pre-planning - identifying intervention personnel who can receive emergency exposures; ensuring they are prepared for the task by provision of training and equipment; making arrangements for medical surveillance and dosimetry that would be required; naming those who would take charge of managing emergency exposures; and specifying limiting dose levels for emergency exposures;

(b)   implementation in the event of a radiation emergency - checking that those who will receive emergency exposures are fit to be exposed and are properly equipped and instructed; managing the exposure of the intervention personnel; ensuring that the limiting dose levels are not exceeded except in extreme situations to save lives; and assessing the doses received in the emergency exposure;

(c)   documenting the emergency exposures - ensuring that dose records are made and kept by approved dosimetry services; providing copies to affected employees; and making a report of the circumstances of emergency exposures and resulting actions.

342   The regulation places a number of duties on employers. This is because the duties refer to employees who may receive emergency exposures, and it needs to be clear that the duties fall on the employers of those employees, whether they be operators, carriers, or others, such as the emergency services. All the requirements that apply to emergency exposures stem from the identification in an emergency plan (ie the operator's, carrier's, or off-site emergency plan, as appropriate) that intervention personnel are likely to receive high doses of radiation, exceeding normal dose limits.

343   The Regulations permit an employee, during a radiation emergency, to receive a dose of ionising radiation in excess of the dose limits in the 1999 Regulations for employees over 18 years of age. This would include employees of the operator, contractors on the premises, carrier and emergency services (notably the fire service). Employees must only be allowed to receive emergency exposures for the purposes of saving life, helping endangered people, preventing large numbers of people from being exposed to ionising radiation, or saving valuable installations or goods. This last circumstance would be particularly important if the integrity of the installation is crucial to

the stability or containment of a radiation source involved in or potentially affected by the radiation emergency. Indeed, emergency exposures may be authorised for on-site intervention personnel before the release of any radioactive substance occurs from the site and before the off-site emergency plan is formally implemented. In this case, dose limits in the 1999 Regulations would still apply to all except the on-site intervention personnel for whom emergency exposures have been formally authorised.

344   In the event of a radiation emergency, the employer (operator, carrier, or emergency service) will need to have people in charge of managing the exposure to ionising radiation of intervention personnel whom they employ. One vital function of such people is to authorise intervention personnel to receive emergency exposures (see regulation 14(1)(g)). Such people need to have appropriate training. During a radiation emergency, the dose limits in the 1999 Regulations will not apply (see guidance paragraphs 390-394 on regulation 15).

(1)   Where an emergency plan prepared pursuant to these Regulations provides for the possibility of any employee receiving an emergency exposure, each employer shall in relation to his employees -

(a)   identify those employees who may be subject to emergency exposures;

345   Each operator and carrier must identify all of their employees who may receive emergency exposures. This may be by name, or by position or role (such as shift charge engineer, driver, or company firefighter). If by position or role, then all individuals having that position or role must be known.

346   Employees of the emergency services who may receive emergency exposures, such as those stationed near to the premises, should be identified. It is virtually impossible to identify emergency service employees who may be likely to receive emergency exposures during a transport incident, unless they were travelling in support vehicles, or a transport incident resulting in a radiation emergency would be likely in their area.

347   Certain groups of employee are not suitable for work involving emergency exposures. These include those listed in regulation 14(5) (ie employees and trainees under 18 years of age, and female employees who are either pregnant or breastfeeding). In other cases, employers should consider whether an individual is suitable, taking account of medical advice where appropriate.

348   It is not necessary for identified employees to be designated as classified persons under regulation 20 of the 1999 Regulations. Radiation emergencies are such rare events that they do not in themselves give rise to a duty to designate classified persons under that regulation. On the other hand it is quite in order to identify people who for their normal work are designated as classified persons.

349   In paragraph 60 of the Approved Code of Practice to the 1999 Regulations, it is recommended that doses received by employees who would not normally be exposed to ionising radiation in the course of their work should be kept below the dose limits which apply to members of the public. It should be noted that the guidance in that paragraph is not relevant to REPPIR and should not be seen as preventing particular individuals being identified for being subject to emergency exposures. No single person is ever likely to experience an emergency exposure more than once in their lifetime (see *Documents of the NRPB*, 1(4), page 3, paragraph 13[19]).

(b) provide such employees with appropriate training in the field of radiation protection and such information and instruction as is suitable and sufficient for them to know the risks to health created by exposure to ionising radiation and the precautions which should be taken;

350 The information, instruction and training received by employees of the operator and carrier must be adequate to fulfil their intervention roles. The degree of training is likely to be comprehensive, and will reflect the level of dose likely to be received. The information and instruction given to employees of the operator are likely to be detailed to enable them to deal with complex installations and technologies on the premises. Information and instruction given to employees of the carrier are likely to be simpler in nature, reflecting more straightforward likely incident scenarios. Information, instruction and training provided for the purposes of regulation 14 is in addition to that provided for those employees who are affected by emergency plans (see guidance to regulations 7(7), 8(8) and 9(14)).

351 The responsibility for provision of information, instruction and training rests with the employer of the employees concerned. However, it is likely that carriers will be able to draw on assistance from consignors for training of their employees (see also regulation 11(3)).

352 Employees of the emergency services who may receive emergency exposures, such as those who would be involved in search and rescue, should also receive adequate information, instruction and training to fulfil their intervention roles. This information, instruction and training is likely to be generic in nature, but should reflect the radiation hazards on site. The duty lies with the emergency service to provide training for its own employees. However, operators should be able to help the emergency services with this (see also regulation 11(3)), and there are benefits from co-ordinating the training of on-site employees with those of the emergency services.

353 For transport incidents, employees of the emergency services local to the incident (who would not have been identified for receiving emergency exposures) will be able to draw on their generic information, instruction and training on dealing with transport incidents involving hazardous (including radioactive) materials. If intervention personnel are drawn from other areas they will also need to rely on generic training.

354 Provision of periodic refresher training and training for newly identified employees who may be subject to emergency exposures also needs to be managed.

(c) provide such equipment as is necessary to restrict the exposure of such employees to radiation;

355 Employees involved in intervention may need equipment to enable them to deal with the incident but which will also enable them to restrict their exposure to ionising radiation. Remote handling tools may be necessary to manipulate sources or to manoeuvre apparatus in high external radiation fields. Employees may need to wear personal protective equipment such as air-fed suits to enable them to enter and work in areas containing high levels of airborne radioactive contaminants. Personal alarm dose monitoring instruments or dose-rate monitoring instruments, suitable for the types of radiation likely to be encountered, should also be provided. In the event of a release of radioactive iodine, doses received by intervention personnel can be restricted by administration, under medical advice, in the form of 'stable iodine' tablets.

356 Equipment provided for the purposes of regulation 14 is in addition to that provided for those employees who are affected by emergency plans (see guidance to regulations 7(7), 8(8) and 9(14)). Arrangements for the issue of equipment for employees receiving emergency exposures should be described in emergency plans.

357 Emergency services may need advice on the suitability of personal protective equipment worn by intervention personnel for protection against radioactive contamination. They are advised to discuss this with the operator (or, if applicable, the carrier or their representative) in the first instance. Other necessary equipment may be provided by the operator or carrier (see also regulation 11(3)).

    (d)   *make arrangements for medical surveillance by an appointed doctor or employment medical adviser to be carried out without delay in the event of a radiation emergency in respect of those employees who receive emergency exposures;*

358 Arrangements for medical surveillance need to be made in advance, but the medical examination need not take place until an emergency exposure has been received (although some classified intervention personnel on the site may have already received medical surveillance under regulation 24 of the 1999 Regulations). Medical surveillance for employees who have been subject to emergency exposures should be carried out by appointed doctors or employment medical advisers, and should include special medical surveillance of any employee who has received an emergency exposure. The nature of the medical surveillance for each individual should take account of the nature of the emergency exposure and that individual's state of health. Any individual who has received an effective dose of ionising radiation in excess of 100 millisieverts in a year, or an equivalent dose of at least twice any relevant dose limit specified in the 1999 Regulations, or in other cases if the appointed doctor (or employment medical adviser) considers this to be necessary in the circumstances, should undergo a special medical examination. The special medical examination may involve counselling the individual and detailing possible restrictions on further exposure.

359 Regulation 24(3) of the 1999 Regulations requires that employers arrange for health records to be kept in respect of employees who are subject to medical surveillance. Such records are not essential for non-classified persons who receive emergency exposures, but employers may find it is useful to keep a record of the medical surveillance that has been conducted using a health record. If so, such a health record would normally be kept until the person to whom it relates has or would have attained the age of 75 years, but in any event for at least 50 years from the date of the last entry made in it. Confidential clinical information should not be recorded in the health record. Note that the Data Protection Act 1998 contains data protection requirements relevant to any such health records, including the right of data subjects to see their health records.

    (e)   *make arrangements with an approved dosimetry service for -*

        (i)   *dose assessments to be carried out without delay in the event of a radiation emergency in respect of those employees who receive emergency exposures, and a dose assessment made for the purpose of this sub-paragraph shall, where practicable, be made separately from any other dose assessment relating to those employees; and*

        (ii)   *the results of the dose assessments carried out under sub-paragraph (i) above to be notified without delay to the employer and to the Executive;*

69

360 Employees who may receive emergency exposures, and who are routinely involved in work with ionising radiation and are classified persons under the 1999 Regulations, will already have arrangements for dose assessments and medical surveillance made for them by their employers. These are likely to be employees of the operator or carrier. Consideration should be given to providing additional dosemeters to these employees (assuming that there is sufficient time to do this) when a radiation emergency is declared, so that doses received during intervention may be assessed separately from routine doses and be recorded separately in the dose record. Employers should be aware that during intervention, there may be significant exposure from routes not covered by the arrangements for routine dosimetry. For example, classified persons may be monitored routinely for exposure only to external radiation, whereas during an emergency exposure they may also receive exposure to internal radiation. In such cases the employer should make suitable arrangements with appropriate approved dosimetry service(s) in addition to the one(s) used for the routine dosimetry.

361 There may be other employees who may receive emergency exposures but who do not routinely have dose assessments or medical surveillance. For a radiation emergency on the premises, this may include:

(a) employees who would only be exposed to ionising radiation during a radiation emergency, such as company firefighters;

(b) employees of contractors on site; and

(c) employees of the emergency services who would be involved in search and rescue.

362 It may not be necessary or reasonable to provide all these employees with dosemeters routinely for use in case of a radiation emergency on the premises. Nevertheless, each employer should make arrangements to ensure that dose assessments can be made with an approved dosimetry service during a radiation emergency, with follow-up medical surveillance as necessary. For example, the operator may arrange to have on the premises a supply of dosemeters that can be distributed to such intervention personnel (who may be employees of the operator, contractors, or emergency services) during a radiation emergency.

363 In the case of transport incidents, it is likely that some employees dealing with the incident (such as those of the fire service local to the incident) will have no dosemeters to hand. Nevertheless, it is still possible to make arrangements for dose assessments to be made for these employees. For example, the carrier could arrange for the consignor's health physics teams to assess the doses of ionising radiation received by the intervention personnel involved in the incident by considering the radiation levels in the area around the incident, the location of those personnel during the intervention, and the duration of their exposure.

364 Arrangements for the issue of dosemeters should be described in emergency plans. Arrangements for dose assessments must be made with an approved dosimetry service, and arrangements need to be in place for the service to notify immediately the results of those assessments to the employer and HSE.

(f) *make arrangements, in respect of dose assessments to be carried out and notified pursuant to sub-paragraph (e) above, to notify the results of such assessments without delay to the appointed doctor or employment medical adviser who is carrying out the medical surveillance on the employee to whom the assessment relates;*

365 Arrangements need to be in place to enable the employer to immediately forward the dose assessments to the approved doctor or employment medical adviser who will be carrying out the medical surveillance.

(g)   identify those employees who shall be authorised, in the event of a radiation emergency, to permit any employee referred to in sub-paragraph (a) above to be subject to an emergency exposure and provide employees who are so authorised with appropriate training.

366 When a radiation emergency occurs, there must be a person in authority who can permit employees to receive emergency exposures:

(a)   for the operator and any contractors on site - this is likely to be someone in a senior position within their own company who is available on the premises at the time of the radiation emergency;

(b)   for the carrier - this is likely to be someone in a senior position who is available at (or can be immediately contacted through) the transport headquarters; and

(c)   for the emergency services - this is likely to be the officer in charge, and decisions should be taken in consultation with the authorised person for the operator or carrier.

367 It is important to note that people authorised to permit employees to receive emergency exposures must themselves be employed by the employer concerned. It follows, for example, that the emergency services must authorise one of their own employees for this function, and cannot rely on someone employed by the operator or carrier.

368 The training provided for people authorised to permit employees to receive emergency exposures is separate from (although related to) the training provided for employees who may receive emergency exposures. The training for authorisations needs to include a good understanding of the effects of high doses of ionising radiation and the risk this entails of deterministic effects (where the severity of the effect is related to the radiation dose, eg skin burns). Such people need to be quite clear as to the restrictions applying to employees who receive emergency exposures (regulation 14(5) and (6)). The training needs to stress the importance of keeping a careful watch on the rate at which employees are exposed, and of keeping to the established dose levels for emergency exposures (see regulation 14(5)(c)) except where the conditions in regulation 14(7) apply.

369 It is recognised that the person authorised to permit employees to receive emergency exposures may not be located close to the incident should this occur. It is likely that the management of the exposure of employees taking part in the intervention may have to be delegated to a person close to the incident (eg forward control point). This person would also need to be suitably trained and experienced to undertake this delegated role.

(2)   An operator shall, at least 28 days before he for the first time commences work with ionising radiation, and a carrier shall at least 28 days before he for the first time undertakes transport of any radioactive substance, or in either case within such shorter time in advance as the Executive may agree, notify to the Executive the dose levels which he has determined are appropriate to be applied in respect of an employee identified for the purposes of paragraph (1)(a) in the event of such emergency.

370 To set dose levels, operators and carriers need to have carried out the hazard identification and risk evaluation required by regulations 4 and 5 to estimate the magnitude of likely doses for personnel in various functions. The dose levels which are determined should normally be set at the maximum of such estimates. However, if the resulting dose levels are seen to be excessively high, then the emergency plan may need to be revised to reduce the estimated dose levels to more tolerable values.

371 The operator must evaluate the dose levels of the emergency exposures that employees may receive to put into effect the operator's emergency plan. The operator would be able to advise the employers of contractors and emergency services on relevant dose levels for their employees.

372 Likewise, the carrier must evaluate the dose levels of the emergency exposures that employees may receive. The carrier would be able to advise the employers of other intervention personnel (identified to receive emergency exposures) on relevant dose levels for their employees, although the need to do this would be rare. The consignor should be able to advise the carrier on appropriate dose levels for a particular consignment.

373 Dose levels would usually be notified to HSE at least 28 days before work with ionising radiation commences. For the carrier, this would be before REPPIR quantities of radioactive substances were transported for the first time (not before each successive transport operation).

374 Dose levels for all intervention personnel (including, for example, emergency services) must be notified to HSE by the operator and carrier. The requirements for emergency plans to cover arrangements for emergency exposures (see Schedule 7) and for consultation on emergency plans (see regulations 7, 8, 9 and 11) together provide the framework for discussions between the operator and carrier and the employers of all intervention personnel regarding emergency exposures.

375 There are nationally agreed dose levels for some emergency services (Home Office/Scottish Office Technical Bulletin 2/93, *Incidents involving radioactive materials*[34]).* However, if the emergency plan envisages doses greater than these nationally agreed levels being received by emergency services personnel, the operator should consult the emergency services as to whether changes to those levels can be established for particular emergency situations, or whether other changes need to be made to the emergency plans to accommodate those nationally agreed levels.

376 The values chosen for dose levels should make allowance for such personal protective equipment as is provided for use in the event of a radiation emergency (see regulation 14(1)(c)). For example, if intervention personnel wear breathing apparatus, which provides uncontaminated air from an independent source, it may safely be assumed that there will be no inhalation of radioactive material during the intervention, and hence the internal dose from this exposure route may be disregarded. With other types of respiratory protective equipment, however, it may not be safe to assume there will be no inhalation of radioactive substances. In such cases, an appropriate protection factor should be used.

377 Additional guidance on doses for emergency exposures is in *Documents of the NRPB*, 1(4), pages 3 and 4, paragraphs 11 to 14.[19]

* *The Scottish Office is now the Scottish Executive.*

(3) Where an operator or carrier determines that a dose level notified under paragraph (2) above is no longer appropriate to be applied in respect of an employee identified for the purposes of paragraph (1)(a) in the event of such emergency, and that a revised level should be determined, the operator or carrier, as the case may be, shall, at least 28 days before formally determining the revised dose level, or within such shorter time in advance as the Executive may agree, notify to the Executive the revised dose level which he considers is appropriate to be applied.

378   Regulation 14(3) provides for dose levels for emergency exposures to be revised if the need arises, perhaps resulting from a material change in the nature of the work undertaken. If the necessary dose level for a particular transport operation is greater than that already notified to and agreed with HSE, then this must be discussed with HSE before that transport operation takes place.

(4)   In any case where in the opinion of the Executive the dose levels for emergency exposure notified pursuant to paragraph (2) or (3) are too high, the operator or carrier shall, if so directed by the Executive, substitute such other dose level or levels as the Executive may consider is appropriate.

379   HSE may decide that the dose levels for the emergency exposures are too high in relation to the likely benefits to be gained. In such cases, HSE may require the employer to change these dose levels. This may have a knock-on effect on the emergency plan, and require the procedures in the plan to be modified so that mitigation is still effective but intervention personnel are exposed to lower doses of ionising radiation.

(5)   Where an emergency plan is put into effect pursuant to the provisions of regulation 13, each employer shall ensure -

(a)   that no employee of his under 18 years of age, no trainee under 18 years of age and no female employee who is pregnant or breastfeeding is subject to an emergency exposure;

(b)   that no other employee of his is subject to an emergency exposure unless -

(i)   that employee has agreed to undergo such exposure;

(ii)   the requirements of paragraph (1)(a) to (f) have been complied with in respect of that employee; and

(iii)   that employee has been permitted to be so by an employee authorised for that purpose under paragraph (1)(g); and

(c)   that no employee of his involved in implementing an emergency plan is exposed to a dose of radiation in excess of the dose level determined in accordance with paragraphs (2), (3) or (4).

380   In the event of a radiation emergency, and when an emergency plan is being implemented in accordance with regulation 13, each employer must put into effect all the arrangements that have been made in respect of emergency exposures for their employees. In particular, and except in circumstances described in regulation 14(7), no employee should be exposed to a dose of ionising radiation greater than the dose level notified to and agreed with HSE. This means that a suitably trained and experienced person close to the incident (eg forward control point) will have to be delegated to manage the exposure of intervention personnel, especially if the person authorised to permit employees to receive emergency exposures is located remotely from the incident.

381 Those employees who have been authorised to permit other employees to receive emergency exposures will need to begin by reviewing the employees who are available to act as intervention personnel, and those available employees will need to agree to receive an emergency exposure (although prior agreement may have been reached during the planning stages). Anyone debarred from receiving an emergency exposure because they are under 18 years of age, or a female employee who is pregnant or breastfeeding, must first be excluded. Then any other employees considered to be unsuitable (see the guidance to regulation 14(1)(a)) should also be excluded. (Employees include the members of the emergency services.)

382 Consideration may need to be given to the exclusion of employees who have been involved in the radiation accident which led to the radiation emergency. Individuals injured or otherwise incapacitated will not be suitable. Individuals who may have been overexposed to ionising radiation (having likely doses greater than the dose limits in the 1999 Regulations) may also be unsuitable, unless it can be confirmed by personal dosimetry that the doses received in the radiation accident do not approach the dose levels for emergency exposures. If any such individuals are permitted to receive emergency exposures, it is recommended that the doses received in the accident be added to the emergency exposure for comparison with the dose levels established under regulations 14(2), (3) or (4).

(6)   The requirement imposed on the employer by paragraph (5)(a) shall not apply in respect of a female employee who is pregnant or breastfeeding until such time as the employee has notified the employer in writing of that fact or the employer should reasonably have been aware of that fact.

383 Prevention of pregnant or breastfeeding employees from receiving emergency exposures depends on the employee informing the employer of her condition. It follows that female employees need to understand the importance of notifying the employer in writing, even if they would prefer to keep their condition completely confidential. Regulation 14 of the 1999 Regulations requires employers of female employees to ensure that they are informed about the possible risks and the importance of informing the employer in writing as soon as they are aware of their pregnancy. This is particularly important where a female employee has been identified under regulation 14(1)(a) of REPPIR as someone who may be subject to emergency exposures.

(7)   The requirement imposed by paragraph (5)(c) shall not apply in respect of an exposure of any employee who -

(a)   being informed about the risks involved in the intervention, agrees to undergo an exposure greater than any dose level referred to in that sub-paragraph for the purpose of saving human life; and

(b)   is permitted to undergo such exposure by an employee authorised by the employer in accordance with paragraph (1)(g) to give such permission.

384 During a radiation emergency, events may not coincide with earlier predictions. In particular, people may be in dire circumstances and in danger of death, and the only way to save their life would be for them to be rescued by intervention personnel. In saving these people, the intervention personnel may be in a situation where they would receive doses of ionising radiation in excess of the dose levels for emergency exposures. In such circumstances, intervention personnel who agree to receive doses in excess of the dose levels may be permitted to do so by the person authorised to permit emergency exposures. Substantial efforts should be made to keep doses to these intervention personnel to levels below those at which serious deterministic

Guidance

14(7)

health effects may occur (*Documents of the NRPB*, 1(4), page 3, paragraph 12[19]). Intervention personnel should only be permitted to receive doses in excess of the dose levels for emergency exposures when the benefits to others outweigh the risks they will incur. Radiation protection advice would be particularly valuable in decision making, and the operator and carrier (or their representative) should be in a position to provide such advice if it were needed.

385   The employer may consider that it would be wise to make a record signed by the employees agreeing to receive, and by the employees permitting them to receive, doses above the dose levels confirming that the individuals concerned were informed about the risks involved in the intervention before agreeing to undergo such emergency exposures, and including the circumstances that justified such exposures in terms of saving human life. This record should be made as soon as possible after the event while the information is fresh in people's minds. It may also be prudent for employers to include information and instruction on intervention involving doses at which serious deterministic health effects may occur alongside the training requirements under regulation 14(1)(b) in readiness in case such a situation arose.

Regulation

14(8)

(8)   Where an employee has undergone an emergency exposure, the employer shall ensure that the dose of ionising radiation received by that employee is assessed by an approved dosimetry service and that the dose assessed is recorded separately in the dose record of that employee or, where no dose record exists, in a record created for the purpose of this paragraph complying with the requirements to which it would be subject if it were a dose record.

Guidance

14(8)

386   Any employee who actually receives an emergency exposure must have that dose recorded in their dose record (see paragraph 387 for guidance on employees who do not have a dose record under the 1999 Regulations). The dose must be recorded so it is clear that it is an emergency exposure, and cannot be confused with a dose of ionising radiation received during routine work with ionising radiation. This applies to emergency exposures of any magnitude, not just those emergency exposures which are greater than the dose limits set in the 1999 Regulations.

387   If an employee actually receives an emergency exposure, and that employee does not normally work with ionising radiation and therefore has no dose record under the 1999 Regulations, then their employer must set up a dose record for them. It is recommended that the employer makes arrangements with an approved dosimetry service to make and keep this dose record.

Regulation

14(9)

(9)   An employer shall at the request of an employee of his in respect of whom a record has been created for the purposes of paragraph (8), and on reasonable notice being given, obtain from the approved dosimetry service and make available to the employee a copy of the record of dose relating to that employee.

Guidance

14(9)

388   This provision allows employees to obtain personal dose monitoring information from the employer, and extends to intervention personnel the right enjoyed by classified persons and others under the 1999 Regulations to be made aware of such information. Employers could produce this information automatically.

Regulation

14(10)

(10)   In the event of a report made pursuant to regulation 13(3) relating to the circumstances of an emergency exposure and the action taken as a result of that exposure, an employer shall keep such report (or a copy thereof) until the person to whom the report relates has or would have attained the age of 75 years but in any event for at least 50 years from the termination of the work which involved any emergency exposure.

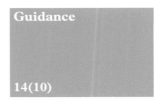

389 Following a radiation emergency, the operator or carrier will have to make a full report of the consequences of the emergency. This should include the emergency exposures, medical surveillance and treatment received by intervention personnel. Any information relating to emergency exposures, medical surveillance or treatment should be kept for the same period of time as the dose records of those personnel.

Regulation 15

Disapplication of dose limits

In the event of a radiation emergency, regulation 11 of the 1999 Regulations shall not apply to intervention.

390 If an event occurs where members of the public are not likely to receive doses of ionising radiation above the levels in Schedule 1, this would not be a radiation emergency and the dose limits in the 1999 Regulations would apply to people engaged in remedial work following such an event.

391 If an event occurs which could lead to a radiation emergency but there has not yet been any release of radioactivity off-site, emergency plans would be implemented (regulations 13(1)(b) and 13(2)(b)), and emergency exposures for intervention personnel may be authorised (regulation 14) to prevent the accident from escalating. Dose limits still apply, but intervention personnel who have been authorised to receive emergency exposures may be exposed to doses in excess of the dose limits in the 1999 Regulations (regulation 11, Schedule 4, Part I, paragraphs 1 and 2). Dose limits would still apply to intervention personnel who have not been authorised to receive emergency exposures, other people on-site (eg staff and visitors) and members of the public.

Disapplication of dose limits

392 If a radiation emergency occurs and members of the public receive doses of ionising radiation in excess of the levels in Schedule 1, then emergency plans would be implemented (regulation 13(1)(a) and 13(2)(a)) and emergency exposures for intervention personnel may be authorised (regulation 14). Intervention personnel who have not been authorised to receive emergency exposures and staff on-site (including people under the age of 18 years and pregnant or breastfeeding women) might receive doses of ionising radiation in excess of the appropriate dose limits in the 1999 Regulations. However, members of the public off-site would already have received doses of ionising radiation in excess of the comparatively much lower levels in Schedule 1 of REPPIR, which are derived from the dose limits for members of the public in the BSS96 Directive. All the dose limits in the 1999 Regulations effectively lose their importance and are therefore disapplied by regulation 15 of REPPIR. Emergency exposures provide the framework within which to manage and control the doses received by intervention personnel who are receiving the highest doses.

393 An employer might not have arrangements in place for emergency exposures because they consider that the intervention personnel dealing with the emergency should not need to exceed the doses in the 1999 Regulations (regulation 11, Schedule 4, Part I, paragraphs 1 and 2). However, if a radiation emergency occurs, staff on-site might receive doses of ionising radiation in excess of the appropriate dose limits in the 1999 Regulations (see introductory guidance to regulation 14 on doses received by employees who may be exposed to ionising radiation as a direct result of the radiation accident that leads to a radiation emergency (covered by regulation 23 of the 1999

Guidance

15

Regulations)). Members of the public would already have received doses of ionising radiation in excess of the dose levels in Schedule 1 of REPPIR. The 1999 Regulations dose limits effectively lose their importance and they are all disapplied by regulation 15 of REPPIR.

Re-application of dose limits

394   Once the intervention (as defined in regulation 2(1)) is complete, the 1999 Regulations dose limits will again apply. The intervention should generally be interpreted as the 'critical' phase of the accident response, as opposed to the recovery phase (see paragraph 139 of the 'Emergency plans' section). Every effort should be made to re-apply the dose limits in the 1999 Regulations in a timely manner, so that exposures to radiation are kept as low as is reasonably practicable (see principles of intervention in Schedule 8, Part I).

Regulation 16

Prior information to the public

Guidance

16

395   The purpose of this regulation is to ensure that any identifiable population group which a radiation emergency (for premises or transport operations, ie rail transport or transferring or conveying through any public place, as defined in regulation 2(1)) could reasonably be expected to affect, is properly informed and prepared in the unlikely event of an emergency occurring. The understanding and co-operation of those affected should enhance the effectiveness of the measures intended for their health protection.

396   Compliance with this regulation should form the starting point of a broader strategy of communication between the operator or carrier whose activity gives rise to the possibility of a radiation emergency and the local community. The greater the extent of this dialogue, the greater are the prospects for those who could be affected retaining the key messages about emergency response. While written communication with the public should always form the foundation of this strategy, it does not preclude the parallel use of other means of communicating. These could include some combination of advertising in the local media, forming local liaison committees, organising exhibitions, holding public meetings and arranging site visits and open days.

397   This regulation is drafted in similar terms to regulation 14 (on information to the public) of COMAH. Where a premises is also subject to regulation 14 of COMAH, it would normally be sensible to present the information about chemical and radiation hazards together.

Regulation

16(1)

(1)   An operator or carrier who carries out work with ionising radiation from which a radiation emergency is reasonably foreseeable shall -

(a)   ensure that members of the public who are in an area in which, in the opinion of the Executive, they are likely to be affected by a radiation emergency arising from the undertaking of that operator or carrier, as the case may be, are supplied, in an appropriate manner, without their having to request it, with at least the information specified in Schedule 9; and

(b)   make that information publicly available.

Guidance

16(1)

398   In the first instance, it is up to each operator or carrier to decide whether a radiation emergency, as defined, is reasonably foreseeable from their work with ionising radiation (see paragraphs 50-51 on the definition of 'radiation emergency' in regulation 2(1) regarding reasonably foreseeable radiation

emergencies). If this is the case, the operator or carrier is required to prepare an emergency plan under regulations 7 or 8, respectively, and also to provide prior information under regulation 16(1). Where a recognised reference accident exists for emergency planning for a nuclear licensed site, then this should be taken as the worst reasonably foreseeable radiation emergency. Where the operator or carrier has decided that a radiation emergency is not reasonably foreseeable, HSE may wish to see how this decision has been reached.

399 Where a radiation emergency is reasonably foreseeable, the operator or carrier should seek from HSE a determination of the area within which prior information is to be distributed. In determining this area, factors that HSE may take into account are:

(a)   the operator's or carrier's assessment of possible accident scenarios, including their likelihood, magnitude and consequences;

(b)   other such assessments as HSE may decide to carry out itself;

(c)   any emergency plans, for example prepared under regulations 7, 8 or 9 of REPPIR, or under licence condition 11 of the site licence for nuclear licensed sites;

(d)   whether there are identifiable population groups likely to be exposed in excess of the Schedule 1 doses as a result of a potential radiation emergency; and

(e)   any geographical factors. For instance, it is not sensible to split a small community for information provision purposes.

400 Once the area has been determined by HSE, the operator or carrier is responsible for informing the public within that area and without them having to ask for it. The information must cover at least the items specified in Schedule 9 (also see the guidance to Schedule 9). It may be appropriate to provide alternative formats of the information, and the operator or carrier could approach the local authority for assistance on identifying members of the public who may require alternative forms of the information. For example, if there is a school for the visually impaired in the planning zone, Braille or audio tapes may be prepared for visually impaired members of the public. The importance of the effective communication of information to children as well as adults should be borne in mind, for example the development of educational packages in schools and colleges and the use of videos. The local authority could also advise if the area contains a significant community whose main language is other than English, in which case the information should be translated for them into the appropriate language(s). This needs to be taken into account as far as is reasonably practicable.

401 The regulation requires the information to be distributed in an appropriate manner. The most common method is to produce booklets for distribution to individual households, often reinforced with a calendar or durable card giving summarised safety instructions. It has to be recognised that in an emergency some people may not find their information booklets quickly. An additional reinforcement is to reproduce the summarised safety instructions in publications that tend to be easily accessible in the home.

402 All the prescribed information does not have to be distributed as a single document. While most of the items of information listed in Schedule 9 are related to the emergency circumstances - and so will vary in detail from one situation to another - paragraph 1 concerns basic facts about radioactivity and

its effects on people and on the environment. For this operators or carriers could, if they wish, use a standard booklet produced by another organisation, as long as it is clear, concise, accurate and appropriate for this application. If separate documents are used in this way, they should still be distributed together.

403 The operator or carrier also has a duty to make the information available to the wider public. This means that any member of the public should be able to obtain the information if they so wish. The operator or carrier should decide how this is to be achieved, for example by direct provision to anyone requesting it or by placing appropriate information in public buildings such as libraries and civic centres (subject to agreement with the occupiers). It is common practice for the full emergency plans of the major nuclear installations to be placed in local libraries. Members of the public contacting the employer or carrier should be informed how the operator or carrier makes the information publicly available, so that they may consult it. Where to place information to achieve wide distribution may vary. It is subject to local needs and requirements. Pilot testing of information could be considered, with local people (see guidance paragraphs 420-427 on regulation 16(6) for suggested ways of publicising information).

404 The information which must be provided is detailed in Schedule 9 but this is the minimum information, and operators and carriers are free to provide more if they wish.

405 One way of distributing information to the public is via the Internet. Operators or carriers may consider placing their information for members of the public on suitable websites. This route, however, may not be used exclusively or as a substitute for the distribution to individual households.

Application to premises

406 For those nuclear installations where detailed emergency planning zones already exist, the determined areas for prior information are at least the size of these zones. As the name suggests, the zones are subject to detailed emergency planning arrangements, particularly for achieving evacuation of the population in them. Those inside the zones are obviously entitled to information. The determined areas will only be larger than these zones where HSE concludes on the basis of the factors described above that there are members of the public outside them who are liable to be affected by a radiation emergency. However, these members of the public outside the zone are only likely to be affected to the extent that they may be asked to shelter.

Application to transport

407 This regulation sets no limitation on the type of work which needs to be assessed for its potential to create a radiation emergency. So, in principle, rail transport activities are included. However, in practice, prior information would only need to be distributed if:

(a) a radiation emergency was reasonably foreseeable from that particular transport operation; and

(b) an identifiable area exists within which members of the public are likely to be affected by the radiation emergency and so should receive the prior information.

408 Transport of radioactive material has been subject over many years to detailed and stringent recommendations from the International Atomic Energy

79

Agency in their publications of regulations for the safe transport of radioactive material, and these recommendations are continually updated. Conformity with these recommendations will obviously be a significant feature in any assessment of a rail transport operation for its potential to create a radiation emergency. There could be occasions when a transport incident does not give rise to an immediate release of radioactivity, but where a release of radiation emergency proportions could follow. While not strictly a situation requiring provision of information under this regulation, the available time should nonetheless be used, as far as circumstances permit, to inform those who could be affected along the lines of the items specified in Schedule 9. This early information should prepare the ground for further dissemination of information, if there were a significant release subsequently.

409   Such an approach would permit an escalating emergency to be handled more logically. Care should be taken to ensure good communication with the public at the outset to avoid creating undue alarm, given that the situation may be quickly resolved.

(2)   In preparing the information to be supplied in accordance with paragraph (1), the operator or carrier shall consult each local authority in the area or areas referred to in that paragraph, any authority likely to fall within paragraph 5 of Schedule 9 and such other persons who seem to him to be appropriate, but the operator or carrier, as the case may be, shall remain responsible for the accuracy, completeness and form of the information so supplied.

410   The operator or carrier must consult the local authority on the preparation of the prior information (see paragraphs 22-25 on the definition of 'local authority' in regulation 2(1)). Consultation with all tiers of local authority is aimed at ensuring the best use of local knowledge and expertise in communicating with the public. Also, in locations where the information provisions of COMAH apply, the local authority can play a co-ordinating role.

411   The authorities likely to be named in the prior information (in Schedule 9, paragraph 5) need to be consulted. The operator or carrier would normally need to include in their consultation the emergency services, health authority/board for the area where the premises are situated, certain Government Departments (in particular: EA, SEPA and DEFRA in England; the Scottish Executive Rural Affairs Department; the Welsh Office, Agriculture Department in Wales), the FSA and the water authority/supplier. Since operators and carriers bear the duty to supply the information to the public, they also have the final responsibility for its accuracy, completeness and form.

(3)   Without prejudice to his duty under paragraph (1), the operator or carrier shall endeavour to enter into an agreement with the local authority in the area referred to in that paragraph for that authority to disseminate the information required to be supplied in accordance with that paragraph to the members of the public mentioned in it.

412   The operator or carrier is required to try to reach agreement with the local authority to distribute prior information to all those in the area determined by HSE (see paragraphs 22-25 on the definition of 'local authority' in regulation 2(1)). Consultation during the preparation stage under regulation 16(2) should help to secure such an agreement with the appropriate level of local authority.

413   There is no duty on the local authority to enter into such an agreement and operators or carriers can only try their best to achieve it. Agreement, if reached, would probably be a commercial contract detailing the services to be

provided and the remuneration for those services. If agreement cannot be reached, then operators or carriers have to make other arrangements to ensure that the information is supplied. Such 'failure to agree' could encompass a mutual wish for operators or carriers to supply the information themselves.

414   Defining which households are to receive information should take account of local road and housing layout. Greater thought is required and special arrangements may be needed for commercial, industrial and public authority premises, shops, hotels, multi-occupied dwellings, campsites etc. Regular visitors to the off-site area, such as those making milk and postal deliveries, also need to be considered. Such people are probably best informed through the base from which they work (for example milk depot, sorting office). Associated local publicity at the time of distribution may help to highlight any shortcomings in the arrangements for other identifiable transient populations. Other options include displaying information in workplaces within the prior information area.

415   In areas with two tiers of local authority, the local authority which is the duty holder for off-site emergency plans and for making arrangements to supply information in the event of a radiation emergency may wish to play a role in the dissemination of prior information and, if so, this could be accommodated by agreement between the parties.

(4)   The operator or carrier shall review and where necessary revise the information referred to in paragraph (1) -

> *(a)   at regular intervals but, in any case, not less than once in three years; and*

> *(b)   whenever significant changes to the emergency measures, action and authorities referred to in paragraphs 3, 4 and 5 of Schedule 9 take place.*

416   Some of the changes that would be considered significant are in:

(a)   major variations in the activities that can give rise to a radiation emergency;

(b)   the system of warning of a radiation emergency;

(c)   the means by which people can continue to keep themselves informed during a radiation emergency;

(d)   the health protection measures themselves;

(e)   the system of distribution of 'stable iodine' tablets;

(f)   the evacuation arrangements;

(g)   the off-site agencies with key responsibilities in implementing the emergency plans; and

(h)   other important features of the emergency plans which will have a practical impact on the population likely to be affected.

(5)   The operator or carrier shall ensure that the information referred to in paragraph (1) is supplied in accordance with that paragraph before carrying out work with ionising radiation to which the assessment made in accordance with regulation 4(1)(a) or (b), as the case may be, applies and that the information is so supplied again and made publicly available -

Regulation 17

Duty of local authority to supply information to the public in the event of a radiation emergency

428 Regulation 17 applies to **ALL** local authorities irrespective of the rest of REPPIR, and it relates to general duties on local authorities to have arrangements to provide information about any kind of radiation emergency. The arrangements may be for the local authority or other organisations to distribute the information.

429 The context of this regulation is planning for situations where an emergency has already occurred. So, as opposed to regulation 16, the foreseeability of the event does not arise. Such planning is easier for premises of known hazard potential, less easy for events of unpredictable location and nature, such as transport incidents or a fallen nuclear powered satellite. If a radiation emergency has not occurred, but an event has occurred which could reasonably lead to a radiation emergency, it is important to avoid creating undue alarm, and care needs to be taken when deciding the appropriate amount of information to be released.

430 The purpose of this regulation is to ensure that those members of the public actually affected by a radiation emergency are informed promptly of the facts of the radiation emergency and the measures that are to be taken for their health protection. The fast moving nature of the situation will almost certainly mean that this information is transmitted verbally, for instance by the police, radio or television. It is important to stress that this regulation is for the benefit of those on whom the protection measures may have a direct impact. It is not concerned with informing the wider public, important though prompt and accurate reporting would be in such circumstances.

431 Reporting arrangements exist under RIMNET* (DTLR led) which includes liaison arrangements with other Member States. Further information is available in *Arrangements for responding to nuclear emergencies*, section 7.[16]

* RIMNET is part of the Government's National Response Plan for dealing with overseas nuclear accidents. It can also be used to support the response to domestic nuclear accidents and for routine monitoring of radioactivity within the UK environment. It provides the facilities necessary to assemble, analyse and interpret the various forms of radiological monitoring data that would be needed to establish the effects of such an accident on the UK.

17

Regulation

17(1)

(1) Every local authority shall prepare and keep up to date arrangements to supply, in the event of any radiation emergency in that local authority's area (howsoever that emergency may arise), information of and advice on the facts of the emergency, of the steps to be taken and, as appropriate, of health protection measures applicable.

17(1)

432 The duty in this regulation is on the local authority which is also the duty holder for off-site emergency plans (see paragraphs 22-25 on the definition of 'local authority' in regulation 2(1)), but also applies to local authorities with no REPPIR premises in their area. This is intended to reinforce the relationship between making arrangements to supply information and emergency planning.

433 For emergency planning at premises, each body that has a role to play in responding to an emergency has its own organisational emergency arrangements. The role of the local authority is to ensure that the arrangements of all the bodies involved are complementary and that the resultant effect of the off-site emergency plan is comprehensive in its coverage (see regulation 9). Precisely the same applies to information provision. The local authority needs to ensure that the arrangements for information provision

of the various bodies involved come together in a complementary and comprehensive way. The summation of these elements then constitutes the 'arrangements'.

434 The local authority will have to make and keep up to date arrangements to supply information and advice in the event of a radiation emergency. There is no requirement for the local authority to prepare the information and advice themselves. For premises, the information and advice will usually be provided by other organisations, as outlined in the organisations' emergency arrangements and the off-site emergency plan. To cope with emergencies that are unpredictable in nature, location and timing, such as transport incidents, the arrangements to inform those affected will of necessity be less detailed and more flexible. Most local authorities already have such arrangements in place.

(2)   The arrangements prepared and kept up to date under paragraph (1) shall provide for the information to be supplied at regular intervals in an appropriate manner, without delay, and without their having to request it, to members of the public who are in that local authority's area and who are actually affected by the radiation emergency.

435 The information arrangements must first and foremost be directed towards those members of the public actually affected by an emergency. This group of people is more precisely defined by regulation 17(5).

436 The arrangements must ensure that, if a radiation emergency occurs, the information must be given to members of the public immediately. The information must continue to be supplied in a way that is regular, appropriate, timely and unprompted. In most cases this will be built around information bulletins relayed on local radio and television stations, which may be supplemented by other means of communication as decisions are taken on health protection measures. For premises with existing off-site emergency plans, agreement may already exist with a local radio or television station as this may have been specified in the prior information. For other radiation emergencies, the police may need a more generic approach so that information can be relayed promptly from the scene of the radiation emergency and so that those affected can be told which station to tune to.

(3)   In preparing those arrangements and keeping them up to date, the local authority shall consult any authority likely to be responsible for implementing the relevant measures referred to in Schedule 10 and such other persons as appear to it to be appropriate.

437 Given the nature of the information arrangements, the consultation required by regulation 17(3) is essential to ensure that the roles played by different authorities dovetail effectively. Organisations likely to require consultation are the local authority involved in dissemination of prior information (if a different tier of local authority), the relevant operators or carriers (or consignors), emergency services, environment agencies, health authorities/boards and certain Government Departments. If appropriate, this could be done as part of the statutory consultation when preparing off-site emergency plans.

438 Although the local authorities must consult any authority responsible for implementing measures, which would include water companies, there is potential for confusion. Local authorities are required by regulation 17 and Schedule 10 to have arrangements in place to inform the public about restrictions on consumption of water supply, but water companies would consider that it is their duty to inform their customers. This issue can be taken into account when the local authority is setting up its arrangements. For

example, local authorities will need to discuss this with water companies and come to a local agreement.

(4)   The information and advice to be supplied in accordance with arrangements prepared and kept up to date under paragraph (1) shall, if relevant to the type of radiation emergency, include that specified in Schedule 10 and shall, in any event, mention the authority or authorities responsible for implementing the relevant measures referred to in that Schedule.

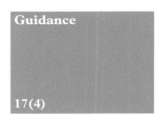

439   This identifies the content of the information to be supplied as being that specified in Schedule 10, but only in so far as it is relevant to the type of radiation emergency that has occurred. So Schedule 10 is more indicative than prescriptive in nature. This contrasts with the prior information required by regulation 16, where the list in Schedule 9 is a minimum requirement. (For further guidance on the content of the information, see guidance to Schedule 10.)

(5)   For the purposes of paragraph (2), the members of the public referred to in that paragraph as actually affected are those whose co-operation is sought to put into effect any steps or health protection measures referred to in paragraph (1).

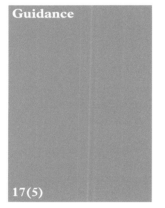

440   The essential purpose of regulation 17 is to supply information to members of the public 'actually affected by a radiation emergency'. Regulation 17(5) serves to define this group of people as those whose co-operation is sought in implementing the health protection measures under the off-site emergency plan. This group of people will include, for example, those asked to shelter, evacuate or take 'stable iodine' tablets (see guidance on Schedule 10, paragraph 2), or refrain from eating or selling foodstuffs they have grown themselves.

441   On the other hand, people living further afield who cannot obtain a particular foodstuff because of restrictions that have been imposed do not meet the definition of being actually affected. This is because the need for their co-operation to put into effect health protection measures does not arise.

Regulation 18

Modifications relating to the Ministry of Defence etc

(1)   In this regulation, any reference to -

(a)   "visiting forces" is a reference to visiting forces within the meaning of any provision of Part 1 of the Visiting Forces Act 1952;[(a)] and

(b)   "headquarters or organisation" is a reference to a headquarters or organisation designated for the purposes of the International Headquarters and Defence Organisations Act 1964.[(b)]

(2)   The Secretary of State for Defence may, in the interests of national security, by a certificate in writing exempt -

(a)   Her Majesty's Forces;

(b)   visiting forces;

(a) 1952 c.67.
(b) 1964 c.5.

(c) any member of a visiting force working in or attached to any headquarters or organisation; or

(d) any person engaged in work with ionising radiation for, or on behalf of, the Secretary of State for Defence,

from all or any of the requirements or prohibitions imposed by these Regulations and any such exemption may be granted subject to conditions and to a limit of time and may be revoked at any time by a certificate in writing.

(3) The requirements of regulation 14 shall not have effect to the extent that this regulation would in the opinion of the Secretary of State for Defence be against the interests of national security.

442 The expectation is that the power in regulation 18(3) would only be applied in relation to MoD personnel serving in an operational context, that is certain members of Her Majesty's Forces.

Regulation 19 — Enforcement and offences

Insofar as any provision of these Regulations is made under section 2(2) of the European Communities Act 1972, sections -

(a) 16 to 21 (approval of codes of practice and enforcement);

(b) 23 (provisions supplementary to sections 21 and 22) and 24 (appeal against improvement or prohibition notice), so far as they relate to an improvement notice;

(c) 26 (power to indemnify inspectors); and

(d) 33 to 42 (provisions as to offences),

of the Health and Safety at Work etc. Act 1974 shall apply to that provision as if that provision had been made under section 15 of that Act.

443 The whole of REPPIR is treated as health and safety regulations under the Health and Safety at Work etc Act 1974 for the purposes of enforcement.

Regulation 20 — Transitional provisions

444 Employers who work with ionising radiation need to consider whether REPPIR applies to them regarding application requirements in regulation 3. The quantities of radionuclides in Schedules 2 and 4 regarding premises and rail transport operations are different from those in Schedule 2, column 6 of the Ionising Radiations Regulations 1985 (the 1985 Regulations). This means that whether employers did or did not have to prepare special hazard assessments under the 1985 Regulations, it does not necessarily mean they will or will not have to prepare reports of assessments under REPPIR.

(1) Where an operator or carrier has carried out work with ionising radiation before the date of the coming into force of these Regulations, an assessment made pursuant to any enactment for the purposes of identifying those matters referred to in sub-paragraphs (c) and (d) of regulation 4(1) shall be deemed to have been made pursuant to regulation 4.

Guidance

20(1)

Regulation

20(2)

Guidance

20(2)

Regulation

20(2)

Guidance

20(2)

Regulation

20(2)

Guidance

20(2)

Regulation

20(2)

445 An operator or carrier who has already undertaken an assessment to identify hazards and evaluate risks (as described in regulations 4(1)(c) and (d)) under other legislation (for example the 1985 Regulations or the 1999 Regulations) is considered to have undertaken that assessment under REPPIR.

(2) Where work with ionising radiation to which these Regulations apply has commenced before the date of the coming into force of these Regulations -

(a) an operator or carrier who is required to send a report of assessment to the Executive under regulation 6(1) shall be deemed to have complied with the requirements of that paragraph if such report is sent to the Executive within 5 months of that date or within such longer time as the Executive may agree;

446 An operator or carrier must send a report of assessment containing the particulars in Schedule 5 to HSE within five months of REPPIR coming into force. The particulars in Schedule 5 are similar to, but not identical to, those in Schedule 7 to the 1985 Regulations. Employers who have already done special hazard assessments under regulation 26 of the 1985 Regulations will, therefore, need to check that they have addressed all the particulars in Schedule 5 of REPPIR.

447 If an operator or carrier considers that they may require more than five months to complete and send their report of assessment to HSE, then they should write to HSE, giving the reasons for the delay, and HSE will consider their request.

(b) an operator who is required to prepare an operator's emergency plan under regulation 7(1) and a carrier who is required to prepare a carrier's emergency plan under regulation 8(1) shall be deemed to have complied with the requirements of that paragraph if that plan is prepared within 6 months of that date or within such longer time as the Executive may agree, and in such case paragraph (3) of regulation 7 or 8 respectively and regulation 9(9) shall not apply;

448 An operator or carrier must complete their emergency plans within six months of REPPIR coming into force. If an operator or carrier considers that they may require more than six months to complete their emergency plan, then they should write to HSE, giving the reasons for the delay, and HSE will consider their request.

(c) an operator who is required to provide information to the local authority in accordance with the requirements of paragraph (4) of regulation 9 shall be deemed to have complied with that paragraph if he provides the required information to the local authority within 6 months of that date or within such longer time as the Executive may agree;

449 An operator must send information to the local authority (to enable the off-site emergency plan to be prepared) within six months of REPPIR coming into force. If an operator considers that they may require more than six months to compile that information, then they should write to HSE, giving the reasons for the delay, and HSE will consider their request. Subsequently, the local authority will need to meet the timing requirements in regulation 9(8) in preparing its off-site emergency plan.

(d) an operator or carrier who is required to notify the Executive of the determined dose levels under regulation 14(2) shall be deemed to have complied with the requirements of that regulation if such notification is

given to the Executive within 5 months of that date or within such longer time as the Executive may agree; and

450   An operator or carrier must notify dose levels for emergency exposures to HSE within five months of REPPIR coming into force. If an operator or carrier considers that they may require more than five months to determine dose levels, then they should write to HSE, giving the reasons for the delay, and HSE will consider their request.

(e)   *subject to paragraph (3) below, an operator or carrier who is required to supply information to the public pursuant to paragraph (1) of regulation 16 shall be deemed to have complied with that paragraph if the information specified in Schedule 9 is supplied within a reasonable time after preparation of the off-site emergency plan or the carrier's emergency plan, as the case may be.*

451   An operator or carrier who has not provided prior information to the public under regulation 3 of PIRER must supply prior information to the public within a reasonable period of time after the off-site/carrier's emergency plan has been prepared.

(3)   *Where prior to the coming into force of these Regulations an operator or carrier has supplied information to the public pursuant to regulation 3 of the Public Information for Radiation Emergencies Regulations 1992,[a] the supply of that information, to the extent that it relates to matters to which these Regulations apply, shall for a period of 3 years from the date upon which it was supplied or, where that information has been updated, the date upon which it was last updated, be deemed to comply with the requirements of regulation 16(1) of these Regulations and for the purposes of these Regulations that information shall be treated as if it had been supplied pursuant to regulation 16(1).*

(a) SI 1992/2997.

452   An operator or carrier who has already provided prior information to the public under regulation 3 of PIRER can consider that information as being supplied under REPPIR. The regular review required under regulation 16(4)(a) of REPPIR will be within three years of the date on which the prior information under PIRER was provided. Necessary changes to the prior information triggered by changes to emergency measures as described in paragraphs 3, 4 and 5 of Schedule 9 to REPPIR would be made under REPPIR, regulation 16(4)(b), as the need arises.

Regulation 21 — Amendment of Regulations

The Regulations referred to in Schedule 11 shall be amended in accordance with the provisions of that Schedule.

Regulation 22 — Revocation and saving

(1)   *The Public Information for Radiation Emergencies Regulations 1992 are revoked, save that -*

(a)   *to the extent that it applies in relation to the transport of radioactive substances by road, inland waterway, sea or air, regulation 3 (Employer or self-employed person to supply prior information) shall continue in force; and*

Regulation
22(1)

Guidance

22(1)

Regulation

22(2)-(3)

Guidance

22(2)-(3)

(b)   *any other provisions of the said 1992 Regulations in so far as is necessary to give effect to regulation 3 shall also continue in force.*

453   Requirements for prior information regarding premises and transport operations (ie rail transport or transferring or conveying through any public place, as defined in regulation 2(1)) are transferred from PIRER, regulation 3, to REPPIR, regulation 16 (and revoked in PIRER).

454   Requirements for prior information regarding other transport modes (road, inland waterway, sea or air) in PIRER, regulation 3, are saved in REPPIR (and not revoked in PIRER). These will subsequently be revoked (see Preface).

455   Requirements for information to the public in the event of a radiation emergency are transferred from PIRER, regulation 4, to REPPIR, regulation 17 (and revoked in PIRER).

(2)   *Paragraph (3) of regulation 41 of the 1999 Regulations is revoked.*

(3)   *To the extent that it applies in relation to the transport of radioactive substances by road, inland waterway, sea or air, regulation 26 (Special hazard assessment) of the Ionising Radiations Regulations 1985^(a) (in this paragraph referred to as "the 1985 Regulations") shall continue in force and, in respect of any employer subject to the said regulation 26, the following provisions shall also continue in force -*

(a)   *paragraphs (1) to (3), (4)(b) and (c) and (5) of regulation 27 (Contingency plans) with the modification that -*

    (i)   *in paragraph (1), the reference to regulation 25(1) of the 1985 Regulations shall be treated as a reference to regulation 7(1) or (2) of the 1999 Regulations;*

    (ii)   *in paragraph (1)(b), the reference to regulation 8(1) of and Schedule 6 to the 1985 Regulations shall be treated as a reference to regulation 16 of the 1999 Regulations;*

    (iii)   *in paragraph (4)(b), the reference to regulation 13(2) of the 1985 Regulations shall be treated as a reference to regulation 21(2) of the 1999 Regulations;*

(b)   *any other provisions of the 1985 Regulations in so far as is necessary to give effect to the provisions specified in this paragraph.*

(a) SI 1985/1333, revoked (subject to a saving) by regulation 41 of the Ionising Radiations Regulations 1999.

456   Requirements for special hazard assessments under the 1985 Regulations, regulation 26, regarding premises and transport operations (ie rail transport and transferring or conveying through any public place, as defined in regulation 2(1)) that had been saved in the 1999 Regulations are now revoked.

457   Requirements for special hazard assessments under the 1985 Regulations, regulation 26, regarding other transport modes (road, inland waterway, sea or air) that had been saved in the 1999 Regulations are now saved in REPPIR. These will subsequently be revoked (see Preface).

Doses of ionising radiation within the meaning of 'radiation emergency'

Regulation 2(1)

1   An effective dose of 5 mSv in the period of one year immediately following the radiation emergency.

2   Without prejudice to paragraph 1 -

(a)   an equivalent dose for the lens of the eye of 15 mSv in the period of one year immediately following the radiation emergency; and

(b)   an equivalent dose for the skin of 50 mSv in the period of one year immediately following the radiation emergency over $1cm^2$ area of skin, regardless of the area exposed.

3   In this Schedule -

(a)   any reference to an effective dose means the sum of the effective dose to the whole body from external radiation and the committed effective dose from internal radiation;

(b)   any reference to equivalent dose to a human tissue or organ includes the committed equivalent dose to that tissue or organ from internal radiation;

(c)   "external radiation" means, in relation to a person, ionising radiation coming from outside the body of that person; and

(d)   "internal radiation" means, in relation to a person, ionising radiation coming from inside the body of that person.

Guidance

458   The purpose of Schedule 1 is to support the definition of a radiation emergency (see paragraphs 52-54 on the definition of radiation emergency in regulation 2(1)).

459   This Schedule deals with doses to members of the public accrued during one year immediately following the radiation emergency. The accrued dose comprises the sum of direct external radiation and internal radiation (eg from inhaling airborne radioactive substances or ingesting contaminated food and drink).

460   In studies that have been done to model radiation emergencies, no reasonably foreseeable scenarios have been identified in which the equivalent dose to the lens of the eye quoted in Schedule 1, paragraph 2(a), is a limiting factor (see NRPB report NRPB-M1311 *Calculations to assist in the revision of IRR-85 with respect to Special Hazard Assessments (REPPIR Schedule 2)*).[25] Unless a particular feature of a radiation accident envisaged in the hazard identification and risk assessment makes a high dose to the lens of the eye a significant feature, it is not anticipated that this dose will be the reason for a radiation emergency being identified.

Specified quantities of radionuclides on premises

Regulation 3(1) and (2)

PART I

Table of radionuclides

Radionuclide name, symbol	Radionuclide form	Quantity (Bq)
Actinium		
Ac-224		$2\ 10^{11}$
Ac-225		$3\ 10^{9}$
Ac-226		$2\ 10^{10}$
Ac-227		$4\ 10^{7}$
Ac-228		$5\ 10^{11}$
Aluminium		
Al-26		$7\ 10^{10}$
Americium		
Am-237		$4\ 10^{12}$
Am-238		$6\ 10^{12}$
Am-239		$2\ 10^{12}$
Am-240		$4\ 10^{12}$
Am-241		$3\ 10^{8}$
Am-242		$1\ 10^{12}$
Am-242m		$3\ 10^{8}$
Am-243		$3\ 10^{8}$
Am-244		$2\ 10^{12}$
Am-244m		$2\ 10^{14}$
Am-245		$2\ 10^{12}$
Am-246		$1\ 10^{12}$
Am-246m		$2\ 10^{12}$
Antimony		
Sb-115		$2\ 10^{12}$
Sb-116		$2\ 10^{12}$
Sb-116m		$2\ 10^{12}$
Sb-117		$1\ 10^{13}$
Sb-118m		$7\ 10^{12}$
Sb-119		$1\ 10^{13}$
Sb-120	(long lived isotope)	$3\ 10^{12}$
Sb-120	(short lived isotope)	$2\ 10^{12}$
Sb-122		$2\ 10^{12}$
Sb-124		$4\ 10^{11}$
Sb-124m		$4\ 10^{12}$
Sb-125		$4\ 10^{11}$
Sb-126		$1\ 10^{12}$
Sb-126m		$2\ 10^{12}$
Sb-127		$2\ 10^{12}$
Sb-128	(long lived isotope)	$2\ 10^{12}$
Sb-128	(short lived isotope)	$1\ 10^{12}$
Sb-129		$2\ 10^{12}$
Sb-130		$1\ 10^{12}$
Sb-131		$2\ 10^{12}$
Argon		
Ar-37	(gas)	$4\ 10^{17}$
Ar-39	(gas)	$2\ 10^{16}$
Ar-41	(gas)	$4\ 10^{13}$

Radionuclide name, symbol	Radionuclide form	Quantity (Bq)
Arsenic		
As-69		$7 \ 10^{11}$
As-70		$1 \ 10^{12}$
As-71		$3 \ 10^{12}$
As-72		$9 \ 10^{11}$
As-73		$8 \ 10^{12}$
As-74		$2 \ 10^{12}$
As-76		$9 \ 10^{11}$
As-77		$2 \ 10^{12}$
As-78		$7 \ 10^{11}$
Astatine		
At-207		$4 \ 10^{12}$
At-211		$2 \ 10^{11}$
Barium		
Ba-126		$2 \ 10^{13}$
Ba-128		$1 \ 10^{13}$
Ba-131		$6 \ 10^{12}$
Ba-131m		$3 \ 10^{12}$
Ba-133		$4 \ 10^{11}$
Ba-133m		$2 \ 10^{12}$
Ba-135m		$2 \ 10^{12}$
Ba-139		$1 \ 10^{12}$
Ba-140		$2 \ 10^{12}$
Ba-141		$1 \ 10^{12}$
Ba-142		$2 \ 10^{12}$
Berkelium		
Bk-245		$3 \ 10^{12}$
Bk-246		$6 \ 10^{12}$
Bk-247		$3 \ 10^{8}$
Bk-249		$2 \ 10^{11}$
Bk-250		$2 \ 10^{12}$
Beryllium		
Be-7		$2 \ 10^{13}$
Be-10		$6 \ 10^{11}$
Bismuth		
Bi-200		$2 \ 10^{12}$
Bi-201		$2 \ 10^{12}$
Bi-202		$3 \ 10^{12}$
Bi-203		$4 \ 10^{12}$
Bi-205		$2 \ 10^{12}$
Bi-206		$2 \ 10^{12}$
Bi-207		$1 \ 10^{11}$
Bi-210		$2 \ 10^{11}$
Bi-210m		$6 \ 10^{9}$
Bi-212		$7 \ 10^{11}$
Bi-213		$7 \ 10^{11}$
Bi-214		$1 \ 10^{12}$

Radionuclide name, symbol	Radionuclide form	Quantity (Bq)
Bromine		
Br-74		$8 \ 10^{11}$
Br-74m		$6 \ 10^{11}$
Br-75		$2 \ 10^{12}$
Br-76		$1 \ 10^{12}$
Br-77		$4 \ 10^{13}$
Br-80		$1 \ 10^{12}$
Br-80m		$5 \ 10^{12}$
Br-82		$3 \ 10^{12}$
Br-83		$2 \ 10^{12}$
Br-84		$7 \ 10^{11}$
Cadmium		
Cd-104		$1 \ 10^{13}$
Cd-107		$4 \ 10^{12}$
Cd-109		$2 \ 10^{12}$
Cd-113		$2 \ 10^{11}$
Cd-113m		$1 \ 10^{11}$
Cd-115		$2 \ 10^{12}$
Cd-115m		$2 \ 10^{12}$
Cd-117		$2 \ 10^{12}$
Cd-117m		$2 \ 10^{12}$
Caesium		
Cs-125		$2 \ 10^{12}$
Cs-127		$1 \ 10^{13}$
Cs-129		$2 \ 10^{13}$
Cs-130		$2 \ 10^{12}$
Cs-131		$6 \ 10^{13}$
Cs-132		$9 \ 10^{12}$
Cs-134		$7 \ 10^{10}$
Cs-134m		$4 \ 10^{12}$
Cs-135		$9 \ 10^{11}$
Cs-135m		$8 \ 10^{12}$
Cs-136		$8 \ 10^{11}$
Cs-137		$1 \ 10^{11}$
Cs-138		$8 \ 10^{11}$
Calcium		
Ca-41		$3 \ 10^{13}$
Ca-45		$3 \ 10^{12}$
Ca-47		$2 \ 10^{12}$
Californium		
Cf-244		$2 \ 10^{12}$
Cf-246		$5 \ 10^{10}$
Cf-248		$2 \ 10^{9}$
Cf-249		$3 \ 10^{8}$
Cf-250		$7 \ 10^{8}$
Cf-251		$3 \ 10^{8}$
Cf-252		$1 \ 10^{9}$
Cf-253		$2 \ 10^{10}$
Cf-254		$4 \ 10^{8}$

Radionuclide name, symbol	Radionuclide form	Quantity (Bq)
Carbon		
C-11		$2\ 10^{12}$
C-11	(vapour)	$1\ 10^{14}$
C-11	(dioxide gas)	$1\ 10^{14}$
C-11	(monoxide gas)	$1\ 10^{14}$
C-14		$3\ 10^{12}$
C-14	(vapour)	$4\ 10^{13}$
C-14	(dioxide gas)	$3\ 10^{15}$
C-14	(monoxide gas)	$1\ 10^{16}$
Cerium		
Ce-134		$1\ 10^{13}$
Ce-135		$2\ 10^{12}$
Ce-137		$2\ 10^{13}$
Ce-137m		$2\ 10^{12}$
Ce-139		$2\ 10^{12}$
Ce-141		$2\ 10^{12}$
Ce-143		$2\ 10^{12}$
Ce-144		$3\ 10^{11}$
Chlorine		
Cl-36		$2\ 10^{12}$
Cl-38		$6\ 10^{11}$
Cl-39		$1\ 10^{12}$
Chromium		
Cr-48		$4\ 10^{13}$
Cr-49		$2\ 10^{12}$
Cr-51		$3\ 10^{13}$
Cobalt		
Co-55		$2\ 10^{12}$
Co-56		$2\ 10^{11}$
Co-57		$1\ 10^{12}$
Co-58		$6\ 10^{11}$
Co-58m		$2\ 10^{13}$
Co-60		$6\ 10^{10}$
Co-60m		$7\ 10^{12}$
Co-61		$2\ 10^{12}$
Co-62m		$9\ 10^{11}$
Copper		
Cu-60		$1\ 10^{12}$
Cu-61		$2\ 10^{12}$
Cu-64		$4\ 10^{12}$
Cu-67		$3\ 10^{12}$
Curium		
Cm-238		$5\ 10^{12}$
Cm-240		$7\ 10^{9}$
Cm-241		$5\ 10^{11}$
Cm-242		$4\ 10^{9}$
Cm-243		$4\ 10^{8}$
Cm-244		$4\ 10^{8}$
Cm-245		$2\ 10^{8}$
Cm-246		$2\ 10^{8}$
Cm-247		$3\ 10^{8}$
Cm-248		$7\ 10^{7}$
Cm-249		$2\ 10^{12}$
Cm-250		$1\ 10^{7}$

Radionuclide name, symbol	Radionuclide form	Quantity (Bq)
Dysprosium		
Dy-155		$1 \ 10^{13}$
Dy-157		$1 \ 10^{14}$
Dy-159		$8 \ 10^{12}$
Dy-165		$2 \ 10^{12}$
Dy-166		$3 \ 10^{12}$
Einsteinium		
Es-250		$1 \ 10^{13}$
Es-251		$6 \ 10^{12}$
Es-253		$8 \ 10^{9}$
Es-254		$2 \ 10^{9}$
Es-254m		$5 \ 10^{10}$
Erbium		
Er-161		$6 \ 10^{12}$
Er-165		$2 \ 10^{14}$
Er-169		$3 \ 10^{12}$
Er-171		$2 \ 10^{12}$
Er-172		$3 \ 10^{12}$
Europium		
Eu-145		$4 \ 10^{12}$
Eu-146		$3 \ 10^{12}$
Eu-147		$4 \ 10^{12}$
Eu-148		$4 \ 10^{11}$
Eu-149		$8 \ 10^{12}$
Eu-150	(long lived isotope)	$1 \ 10^{11}$
Eu-150	(short lived isotope)	$2 \ 10^{12}$
Eu-152		$1 \ 10^{11}$
Eu-152m		$2 \ 10^{12}$
Eu-154		$1 \ 10^{11}$
Eu-155		$2 \ 10^{12}$
Eu-156		$2 \ 10^{12}$
Eu-157		$2 \ 10^{12}$
Eu-158		$1 \ 10^{12}$
Fermium		
Fm-252		$7 \ 10^{10}$
Fm-253		$6 \ 10^{10}$
Fm-254		$3 \ 10^{11}$
Fm-255		$9 \ 10^{10}$
Fm-257		$3 \ 10^{9}$
Fluorine		
F-18		$2 \ 10^{12}$
Francium		
Fr-222		$1 \ 10^{12}$
Fr-223		$2 \ 10^{12}$
Gadolinium		
Gd-145		$2 \ 10^{12}$
Gd-146		$2 \ 10^{12}$
Gd-147		$5 \ 10^{12}$
Gd-148		$9 \ 10^{8}$
Gd-149		$6 \ 10^{12}$
Gd-151		$5 \ 10^{12}$
Gd-152		$1 \ 10^{9}$
Gd-153		$2 \ 10^{12}$
Gd-159		$2 \ 10^{12}$

Radionuclide name, symbol	Radionuclide form	Quantity (Bq)
Gallium		
Ga-65		$1 \ 10^{12}$
Ga-66		$9 \ 10^{11}$
Ga-67		$5 \ 10^{12}$
Ga-68		$2 \ 10^{12}$
Ga-70		$1 \ 10^{12}$
Ga-72		$2 \ 10^{12}$
Ga-73		$2 \ 10^{12}$
Germanium		
Ge-66		$3 \ 10^{12}$
Ge-67		$7 \ 10^{11}$
Ge-68		$1 \ 10^{12}$
Ge-69		$2 \ 10^{12}$
Ge-71		$7 \ 10^{14}$
Ge-75		$2 \ 10^{12}$
Ge-77		$1 \ 10^{12}$
Ge-78		$2 \ 10^{12}$
Gold		
Au-193		$7 \ 10^{12}$
Au-194		$1 \ 10^{13}$
Au-195		$3 \ 10^{12}$
Au-198		$2 \ 10^{12}$
Au-198m		$2 \ 10^{12}$
Au-199		$3 \ 10^{12}$
Au-200		$1 \ 10^{12}$
Au-200m		$2 \ 10^{12}$
Au-201		$2 \ 10^{12}$
Hafnium		
Hf-170		$4 \ 10^{12}$
Hf-172		$5 \ 10^{11}$
Hf-173		$6 \ 10^{12}$
Hf-175		$2 \ 10^{12}$
Hf-177m		$2 \ 10^{12}$
Hf-178m		$4 \ 10^{10}$
Hf-179m		$2 \ 10^{12}$
Hf-180m		$2 \ 10^{12}$
Hf-181		$1 \ 10^{12}$
Hf-182		$7 \ 10^{10}$
Hf-182m		$2 \ 10^{12}$
Hf-183		$2 \ 10^{12}$
Hf-184		$2 \ 10^{12}$
Holmium		
Ho-155		$2 \ 10^{12}$
Ho-157		$4 \ 10^{12}$
Ho-159		$6 \ 10^{12}$
Ho-161		$1 \ 10^{13}$
Ho-162		$5 \ 10^{12}$
Ho-162m		$4 \ 10^{12}$
Ho-164		$2 \ 10^{12}$
Ho-164m		$4 \ 10^{12}$
Ho-166		$1 \ 10^{12}$
Ho-166m		$8 \ 10^{10}$
Ho-167		$2 \ 10^{12}$

Radionuclide name, symbol	Radionuclide form	Quantity (Bq)
Hydrogen		
H-3	(tritiated water)	$7\ 10^{13}$
H-3	(organically bound tritium)	$1\ 10^{14}$
H-3	(tritiated water vapour)	$1\ 10^{15}$
H-3	(gas)	$1\ 10^{18}$
H-3	(tritiated methane gas)	$1\ 10^{17}$
H-3	(organically bound tritium gas/vapour)	$6\ 10^{14}$
Indium		
In-109		$7\ 10^{12}$
In-110	(long lived isotope)	$2\ 10^{13}$
In-110	(short lived isotope)	$1\ 10^{12}$
In-111		$9\ 10^{12}$
In-112		$2\ 10^{12}$
In-113m		$5\ 10^{12}$
In-114		$1\ 10^{12}$
In-114m		$9\ 10^{11}$
In-115		$6\ 10^{10}$
In-115m		$3\ 10^{12}$
In-116m		$2\ 10^{12}$
In-117		$2\ 10^{12}$
In-117m		$2\ 10^{12}$
In-119m		$9\ 10^{11}$

Radionuclide name, symbol	Radionuclide form	Quantity (Bq)
Iodine		
I-120		$6\ 10^{11}$
I-120	(elemental vapour)	$2\ 10^{13}$
I-120	(methyl iodide vapour)	$2\ 10^{13}$
I-120m		$7\ 10^{11}$
I-120m	(elemental vapour)	$2\ 10^{13}$
I-120m	(methyl iodide vapour)	$2\ 10^{13}$
I-121		$4\ 10^{12}$
I-121	(elemental vapour)	$1\ 10^{14}$
I-121	(methyl iodide vapour)	$1\ 10^{14}$
I-123		$9\ 10^{12}$
I-123	(elemental vapour)	$5\ 10^{13}$
I-123	(methyl iodide vapour)	$6\ 10^{13}$
I-124		$2\ 10^{12}$
I-124	(elemental vapour)	$9\ 10^{11}$
I-124	(methyl iodide vapour)	$1\ 10^{12}$
I-125		$1\ 10^{11}$
I-125	(elemental vapour)	$1\ 10^{12}$
I-125	(methyl iodide vapour)	$1\ 10^{12}$
I-126		$8\ 10^{11}$
I-126	(elemental vapour)	$5\ 10^{11}$
I-126	(methyl iodide vapour)	$6\ 10^{11}$
I-128		$1\ 10^{12}$
I-128	(elemental vapour)	$2\ 10^{14}$
I-128	(methyl iodide vapour)	$5\ 10^{14}$
I-129		$1\ 10^{10}$
I-129	(elemental vapour)	$2\ 10^{11}$
I-129	(methyl iodide vapour)	$2\ 10^{11}$
I-130		$3\ 10^{12}$
I-130	(elemental vapour)	$5\ 10^{12}$
I-130	(methyl iodide vapour)	$6\ 10^{12}$
I-131		$9\ 10^{10}$
I-131	(elemental vapour)	$6\ 10^{11}$
I-131	(methyl iodide vapour)	$7\ 10^{11}$
I-132		$2\ 10^{12}$
I-132	(elemental vapour)	$2\ 10^{13}$
I-132	(methyl iodide vapour)	$3\ 10^{13}$
I-132m		$2\ 10^{12}$
I-132m	(elemental vapour)	$4\ 10^{13}$
I-132m	(methyl iodide vapour)	$5\ 10^{13}$
I-133		$2\ 10^{12}$
I-133	(elemental vapour)	$2\ 10^{12}$
I-133	(methyl iodide vapour)	$3\ 10^{12}$
I-134		$2\ 10^{12}$
I-134	(elemental vapour)	$3\ 10^{13}$
I-134	(methyl iodide vapour)	$4\ 10^{13}$
I-135		$2\ 10^{12}$
I-135	(elemental vapour)	$9\ 10^{12}$
I-135	(methyl iodide vapour)	$1\ 10^{13}$

Radionuclide name, symbol	Radionuclide form	Quantity (Bq)
Iridium		
Ir-182		$1 \ 10^{12}$
Ir-184		$2 \ 10^{12}$
Ir-185		$3 \ 10^{12}$
Ir-186	(long lived isotope)	$3 \ 10^{12}$
Ir-186	(short lived isotope)	$2 \ 10^{12}$
Ir-187		$6 \ 10^{12}$
Ir-188		$5 \ 10^{12}$
Ir-189		$9 \ 10^{12}$
Ir-190		$2 \ 10^{12}$
Ir-190m	(long lived isotope)	$3 \ 10^{12}$
Ir-190m	(short lived isotope)	$1 \ 10^{13}$
Ir-192		$6 \ 10^{11}$
Ir-192m		$4 \ 10^{11}$
Ir-193m		$4 \ 10^{12}$
Ir-194		$1 \ 10^{12}$
Ir-194m		$1 \ 10^{11}$
Ir-195		$2 \ 10^{12}$
Ir-195m		$2 \ 10^{12}$
Iron		
Fe-52		$2 \ 10^{12}$
Fe-55		$8 \ 10^{12}$
Fe-59		$8 \ 10^{11}$
Fe-60		$4 \ 10^{10}$
Krypton		
Kr-74	(gas)	$5 \ 10^{13}$
Kr-76	(gas)	$1 \ 10^{14}$
Kr-77	(gas)	$6 \ 10^{13}$
Kr-79	(gas)	$2 \ 10^{14}$
Kr-81	(gas)	$7 \ 10^{15}$
Kr-81m	(gas)	$5 \ 10^{14}$
Kr-83m	(gas)	$3 \ 10^{16}$
Kr-85	(gas)	$1 \ 10^{16}$
Kr-85m	(gas)	$4 \ 10^{14}$
Kr-87	(gas)	$7 \ 10^{13}$
Kr-88	(gas)	$3 \ 10^{13}$
Lanthanum		
La-131		$2 \ 10^{12}$
La-132		$2 \ 10^{12}$
La-135		$2 \ 10^{14}$
La-137		$2 \ 10^{12}$
La-138		$2 \ 10^{11}$
La-140		$2 \ 10^{12}$
La-141		$1 \ 10^{12}$
La-142		$1 \ 10^{12}$
La-143		$7 \ 10^{11}$

Radionuclide name, symbol	Radionuclide form	Quantity (Bq)
Lead		
Pb-195m		$2 \ 10^{12}$
Pb-198		$4 \ 10^{12}$
Pb-199		$6 \ 10^{12}$
Pb-200		$3 \ 10^{12}$
Pb-201		$8 \ 10^{12}$
Pb-202		$6 \ 10^{11}$
Pb-202m		$4 \ 10^{12}$
Pb-203		$9 \ 10^{12}$
Pb-205		$1 \ 10^{13}$
Pb-209		$2 \ 10^{12}$
Pb-210		$3 \ 10^{9}$
Pb-211		$2 \ 10^{12}$
Pb-212		$1 \ 10^{11}$
Pb-214		$1 \ 10^{12}$
Lutetium		
Lu-169		$6 \ 10^{12}$
Lu-170		$3 \ 10^{12}$
Lu-171		$4 \ 10^{12}$
Lu-172		$3 \ 10^{12}$
Lu-173		$2 \ 10^{12}$
Lu-174		$1 \ 10^{12}$
Lu-174m		$3 \ 10^{12}$
Lu-176		$3 \ 10^{11}$
Lu-176m		$2 \ 10^{12}$
Lu-177		$3 \ 10^{12}$
Lu-177m		$3 \ 10^{11}$
Lu-178		$1 \ 10^{12}$
Lu-178m		$1 \ 10^{12}$
Lu-179		$2 \ 10^{12}$
Magnesium		
Mg-28		$5 \ 10^{12}$
Manganese		
Mn-51		$1 \ 10^{12}$
Mn-52		$2 \ 10^{12}$
Mn-52m		$8 \ 10^{11}$
Mn-53		$1 \ 10^{14}$
Mn-54		$3 \ 10^{11}$
Mn-56		$1 \ 10^{12}$
Mendelevium		
Md-257		$9 \ 10^{11}$
Md-258		$4 \ 10^{9}$

Radionuclide name, symbol	Radionuclide form	Quantity (Bq)
Mercury		
Hg-193	(organic)	$3 \ 10^{12}$
Hg-193	(inorganic)	$3 \ 10^{12}$
Hg-193	(vapour)	$2 \ 10^{13}$
Hg-193m	(organic)	$2 \ 10^{12}$
Hg-193m	(inorganic)	$2 \ 10^{12}$
Hg-193m	(vapour)	$6 \ 10^{12}$
Hg-194	(organic)	$3 \ 10^{11}$
Hg-194	(inorganic)	$1 \ 10^{12}$
Hg-194	(vapour)	$6 \ 10^{11}$
Hg-195	(organic)	$5 \ 10^{12}$
Hg-195	(inorganic)	$5 \ 10^{12}$
Hg-195	(vapour)	$1 \ 10^{13}$
Hg-195m	(organic)	$3 \ 10^{12}$
Hg-195m	(inorganic)	$3 \ 10^{12}$
Hg-195m	(vapour)	$3 \ 10^{12}$
Hg-197	(organic)	$7 \ 10^{12}$
Hg-197	(inorganic)	$7 \ 10^{12}$
Hg-197	(vapour)	$5 \ 10^{12}$
Hg-197m	(organic)	$2 \ 10^{12}$
Hg-197m	(inorganic)	$2 \ 10^{12}$
Hg-197m	(vapour)	$4 \ 10^{12}$
Hg-199m	(organic)	$2 \ 10^{12}$
Hg-199m	(inorganic)	$2 \ 10^{12}$
Hg-199m	(vapour)	$1 \ 10^{14}$
Hg-203	(organic)	$3 \ 10^{12}$
Hg-203	(inorganic)	$3 \ 10^{12}$
Hg-203	(vapour)	$3 \ 10^{12}$
Molybdenum		
Mo-90		$2 \ 10^{12}$
Mo-93		$2 \ 10^{12}$
Mo-93m		$4 \ 10^{12}$
Mo-99		$2 \ 10^{12}$
Mo-101		$2 \ 10^{12}$
Neodymium		
Nd-136		$4 \ 10^{12}$
Nd-138		$5 \ 10^{13}$
Nd-139		$2 \ 10^{12}$
Nd-139m		$3 \ 10^{12}$
Nd-141		$2 \ 10^{13}$
Nd-147		$2 \ 10^{12}$
Nd-149		$2 \ 10^{12}$
Nd-151		$1 \ 10^{12}$
Neon		
Ne-19	(gas)	$6 \ 10^{13}$
Neptunium		
Np-232		$3 \ 10^{12}$
Np-233		$2 \ 10^{14}$
Np-234		$5 \ 10^{12}$
Np-235		$2 \ 10^{13}$
Np-236	(long lived isotope)	$3 \ 10^{9}$
Np-236	(short lived isotope)	$3 \ 10^{12}$
Np-237		$5 \ 10^{8}$
Np-238		$2 \ 10^{12}$
Np-239		$1 \ 10^{12}$
Np-240		$7 \ 10^{11}$

Radionuclide name, symbol	Radionuclide form	Quantity (Bq)
Nickel		
Ni-56		$4\ 10^{12}$
Ni-56	(carbonyl vapour)	$1\ 10^{13}$
Ni-57		$2\ 10^{12}$
Ni-57	(carbonyl vapour)	$2\ 10^{13}$
Ni-59		$4\ 10^{13}$
Ni-59	(carbonyl vapour)	$2\ 10^{13}$
Ni-63		$1\ 10^{13}$
Ni-63	(carbonyl vapour)	$1\ 10^{13}$
Ni-65		$1\ 10^{12}$
Ni-65	(carbonyl vapour)	$4\ 10^{13}$
Ni-66		$5\ 10^{12}$
Ni-66	(carbonyl vapour)	$1\ 10^{13}$
Niobium		
Nb-88		$7\ 10^{11}$
Nb-89	(long lived isotope)	$1\ 10^{12}$
Nb-89	(short lived isotope)	$8\ 10^{11}$
Nb-90		$2\ 10^{12}$
Nb-93m		$1\ 10^{13}$
Nb-94		$1\ 10^{11}$
Nb-95		$2\ 10^{12}$
Nb-95m		$2\ 10^{12}$
Nb-96		$2\ 10^{12}$
Nb-97		$2\ 10^{12}$
Nb-98		$1\ 10^{12}$
Nitrogen		
N-13	(gas)	$6\ 10^{13}$
Osmium		
Os-180		$1\ 10^{13}$
Os-181		$3\ 10^{12}$
Os-182		$6\ 10^{12}$
Os-185		$7\ 10^{11}$
Os-189m		$1\ 10^{13}$
Os-191		$4\ 10^{12}$
Os-191m		$7\ 10^{12}$
Os-193		$2\ 10^{12}$
Os-194		$2\ 10^{11}$
Palladium		
Pd-100		$7\ 10^{12}$
Pd-101		$8\ 10^{12}$
Pd-103		$4\ 10^{13}$
Pd-107		$3\ 10^{13}$
Pd-109		$2\ 10^{12}$
Phosphorus		
P-32		$1\ 10^{11}$
P-33		$3\ 10^{12}$

Radionuclide name, symbol	Radionuclide form	Quantity (Bq)
Platinum		
Pt-186		$9\ 10^{13}$
Pt-188		$6\ 10^{12}$
Pt-189		$6\ 10^{12}$
Pt-191		$7\ 10^{12}$
Pt-193		$1\ 10^{14}$
Pt-193m		$3\ 10^{12}$
Pt-195m		$3\ 10^{12}$
Pt-197		$2\ 10^{12}$
Pt-197m		$2\ 10^{12}$
Pt-199		$2\ 10^{12}$
Pt-200		$2\ 10^{12}$
Plutonium		
Pu-234		$1\ 10^{12}$
Pu-235		$2\ 10^{13}$
Pu-236		$6\ 10^{8}$
Pu-237		$1\ 10^{13}$
Pu-238		$2\ 10^{8}$
Pu-239		$2\ 10^{8}$
Pu-240		$2\ 10^{8}$
Pu-241		$1\ 10^{10}$
Pu-242		$2\ 10^{8}$
Pu-243		$2\ 10^{12}$
Pu-244		$2\ 10^{8}$
Pu-245		$2\ 10^{12}$
Pu-246		$2\ 10^{12}$
Polonium		
Po-203		$3\ 10^{12}$
Po-205		$7\ 10^{12}$
Po-206		$1\ 10^{11}$
Po-207		$8\ 10^{12}$
Po-208		$2\ 10^{9}$
Po-209		$2\ 10^{9}$
Po-210		$4\ 10^{9}$
Potassium		
K-40		$2\ 10^{12}$
K-42		$7\ 10^{11}$
K-43		$2\ 10^{12}$
K-44		$6\ 10^{11}$
K-45		$9\ 10^{11}$
Praseodymium		
Pr-136		$1\ 10^{12}$
Pr-137		$2\ 10^{12}$
Pr-138m		$2\ 10^{12}$
Pr-139		$7\ 10^{12}$
Pr-142		$1\ 10^{12}$
Pr-142m		$2\ 10^{15}$
Pr-143		$2\ 10^{12}$
Pr-144		$2\ 10^{12}$
Pr-145		$1\ 10^{12}$
Pr-147		$1\ 10^{12}$

Radionuclide name, symbol	Radionuclide form	Quantity (Bq)
Promethium		
Pm-141		$1\ 10^{12}$
Pm-143		$9\ 10^{11}$
Pm-144		$2\ 10^{11}$
Pm-145		$3\ 10^{12}$
Pm-146		$2\ 10^{11}$
Pm-147		$4\ 10^{12}$
Pm-148		$1\ 10^{12}$
Pm-148m		$5\ 10^{11}$
Pm-149		$2\ 10^{12}$
Pm-150		$1\ 10^{12}$
Pm-151		$2\ 10^{12}$
Protactinium		
Pa-227		$3\ 10^{11}$
Pa-228		$3\ 10^{11}$
Pa-230		$3\ 10^{10}$
Pa-231		$2\ 10^{8}$
Pa-232		$2\ 10^{12}$
Pa-233		$2\ 10^{12}$
Pa-234		$5\ 10^{11}$
Radium		
Ra-223		$3\ 10^{9}$
Ra-224		$7\ 10^{9}$
Ra-225		$3\ 10^{9}$
Ra-226		$2\ 10^{9}$
Ra-227		$2\ 10^{12}$
Ra-228		$1\ 10^{9}$
Rhenium		
Re-177		$2\ 10^{12}$
Re-178		$2\ 10^{12}$
Re-181		$3\ 10^{12}$
Re-182	(long lived isotope)	$2\ 10^{12}$
Re-182	(short lived isotope)	$4\ 10^{12}$
Re-184		$1\ 10^{12}$
Re-184m		$7\ 10^{11}$
Re-186		$2\ 10^{12}$
Re-186m		$1\ 10^{12}$
Re-187		$5\ 10^{14}$
Re-188		$1\ 10^{12}$
Re-188m		$3\ 10^{12}$
Re-189		$2\ 10^{12}$
Rhodium		
Rh-99		$4\ 10^{12}$
Rh-99m		$9\ 10^{12}$
Rh-100		$4\ 10^{12}$
Rh-101		$7\ 10^{11}$
Rh-101m		$2\ 10^{13}$
Rh-102		$1\ 10^{11}$
Rh-102m		$6\ 10^{11}$
Rh-103m		$3\ 10^{15}$
Rh-105		$2\ 10^{12}$
Rh-106m		$2\ 10^{12}$
Rh-107		$2\ 10^{12}$

Radionuclide name, symbol	Radionuclide form	Quantity (Bq)
Rubidium		
Rb-79		$1\ 10^{12}$
Rb-81		$2\ 10^{12}$
Rb-81m		$4\ 10^{12}$
Rb-82m		$3\ 10^{12}$
Rb-83		$1\ 10^{12}$
Rb-84		$1\ 10^{12}$
Rb-86		$2\ 10^{11}$
Rb-87		$4\ 10^{12}$
Rb-88		$5\ 10^{11}$
Rb-89		$9\ 10^{11}$
Ruthenium		
Ru-94		$1\ 10^{14}$
Ru-94	(tetroxide vapour)	$1\ 10^{14}$
Ru-97		$3\ 10^{13}$
Ru-97	(tetroxide vapour)	$1\ 10^{14}$
Ru-103		$2\ 10^{12}$
Ru-103	(tetroxide vapour)	$1\ 10^{13}$
Ru-105		$2\ 10^{12}$
Ru-105	(tetroxide vapour)	$6\ 10^{13}$
Ru-106		$3\ 10^{11}$
Ru-106	(tetroxide vapour)	$8\ 10^{11}$
Samarium		
Sm-141		$1\ 10^{12}$
Sm-141m		$2\ 10^{12}$
Sm-142		$9\ 10^{12}$
Sm-145		$3\ 10^{12}$
Sm-146		$2\ 10^{9}$
Sm-147		$3\ 10^{9}$
Sm-151		$6\ 10^{12}$
Sm-153		$2\ 10^{12}$
Sm-155		$2\ 10^{12}$
Sm-156		$2\ 10^{12}$
Scandium		
Sc-43		$2\ 10^{12}$
Sc-44		$2\ 10^{12}$
Sc-44m		$9\ 10^{12}$
Sc-46		$3\ 10^{11}$
Sc-47		$3\ 10^{12}$
Sc-48		$2\ 10^{12}$
Sc-49		$1\ 10^{12}$
Selenium		
Se-70		$2\ 10^{12}$
Se-73		$2\ 10^{12}$
Se-73m		$2\ 10^{12}$
Se-75		$2\ 10^{11}$
Se-79		$5\ 10^{10}$
Se-81		$2\ 10^{12}$
Se-81m		$4\ 10^{12}$
Se-83		$2\ 10^{12}$
Silicon		
Si-31		$2\ 10^{12}$
Si-32		$2\ 10^{11}$

Radionuclide name, symbol	Radionuclide form	Quantity (Bq)
Silver		
Ag-102		$1\ 10^{12}$
Ag-103		$2\ 10^{12}$
Ag-104		$3\ 10^{12}$
Ag-104m		$2\ 10^{12}$
Ag-105		$2\ 10^{12}$
Ag-106		$2\ 10^{12}$
Ag-106m		$2\ 10^{12}$
Ag-108m		$1\ 10^{11}$
Ag-110m		$3\ 10^{10}$
Ag-111		$2\ 10^{12}$
Ag-112		$7\ 10^{11}$
Ag-115		$9\ 10^{11}$
Sodium		
Na-22		$1\ 10^{11}$
Na-24		$2\ 10^{12}$
Strontium		
Sr-80		$1\ 10^{14}$
Sr-81		$9\ 10^{11}$
Sr-82		$2\ 10^{12}$
Sr-83		$3\ 10^{12}$
Sr-85		$1\ 10^{12}$
Sr-85m		$3\ 10^{13}$
Sr-87m		$7\ 10^{12}$
Sr-89		$1\ 10^{12}$
Sr-90		$8\ 10^{10}$
Sr-91		$2\ 10^{12}$
Sr-92		$2\ 10^{12}$
Sulphur		
S-35	(inorganic)	$1\ 10^{12}$
S-35	(organic)	$2\ 10^{11}$
S-35	(carbon disulphide vapour)	$2\ 10^{13}$
S-35	(vapour)	$2\ 10^{14}$
S-35	(dioxide gas)	$1\ 10^{14}$
Tantalum		
Ta-172		$2\ 10^{12}$
Ta-173		$2\ 10^{12}$
Ta-174		$2\ 10^{12}$
Ta-175		$2\ 10^{12}$
Ta-176		$3\ 10^{12}$
Ta-177		$1\ 10^{13}$
Ta-178	(long lived isotope)	$3\ 10^{12}$
Ta-179		$6\ 10^{12}$
Ta-180		$9\ 10^{11}$
Ta-180m		$6\ 10^{12}$
Ta-182		$3\ 10^{11}$
Ta-182m		$2\ 10^{12}$
Ta-183		$2\ 10^{12}$
Ta-184		$2\ 10^{12}$
Ta-185		$1\ 10^{12}$
Ta-186		$9\ 10^{11}$

Radionuclide name, symbol	Radionuclide form	Quantity (Bq)
Technetium		
Tc-93		$5\ 10^{13}$
Tc-93m		$4\ 10^{12}$
Tc-94		$6\ 10^{12}$
Tc-94m		$1\ 10^{12}$
Tc-95		$4\ 10^{13}$
Tc-95m		$1\ 10^{12}$
Tc-96		$4\ 10^{12}$
Tc-96m		$2\ 10^{13}$
Tc-97		$9\ 10^{12}$
Tc-97m		$5\ 10^{12}$
Tc-98		$1\ 10^{11}$
Tc-99		$5\ 10^{10}$
Tc-99m		$1\ 10^{13}$
Tc-101		$2\ 10^{12}$
Tc-104		$6\ 10^{11}$
Tellurium		
Te-116		$6\ 10^{12}$
Te-116	(vapour)	$2\ 10^{14}$
Te-121		$4\ 10^{12}$
Te-121	(vapour)	$3\ 10^{13}$
Te-121m		$1\ 10^{12}$
Te-121m	(vapour)	$3\ 10^{12}$
Te-123		$6\ 10^{12}$
Te-123	(vapour)	$2\ 10^{12}$
Te-123m		$2\ 10^{12}$
Te-123m	(vapour)	$5\ 10^{12}$
Te-125m		$2\ 10^{12}$
Te-125m	(vapour)	$8\ 10^{12}$
Te-127		$2\ 10^{12}$
Te-127	(vapour)	$2\ 10^{14}$
Te-127m		$1\ 10^{12}$
Te-127m	(vapour)	$2\ 10^{12}$
Te-129		$2\ 10^{12}$
Te-129	(vapour)	$4\ 10^{14}$
Te-129m		$1\ 10^{12}$
Te-129m	(vapour)	$3\ 10^{12}$
Te-131		$1\ 10^{12}$
Te-131	(vapour)	$1\ 10^{14}$
Te-131m		$2\ 10^{12}$
Te-131m	(vapour)	$5\ 10^{12}$
Te-132		$3\ 10^{12}$
Te-132	(vapour)	$2\ 10^{12}$
Te-133		$1\ 10^{12}$
Te-133	(vapour)	$7\ 10^{13}$
Te-133m		$1\ 10^{12}$
Te-133m	(vapour)	$2\ 10^{13}$
Te-134		$3\ 10^{12}$
Te-134	(vapour)	$7\ 10^{13}$

Radionuclide name, symbol	Radionuclide form	Quantity (Bq)
Terbium		
Tb-147		$2\ 10^{12}$
Tb-149		$2\ 10^{12}$
Tb-150		$2\ 10^{12}$
Tb-151		$4\ 10^{12}$
Tb-153		$7\ 10^{12}$
Tb-154		$4\ 10^{12}$
Tb-155		$1\ 10^{13}$
Tb-156		$3\ 10^{12}$
Tb-156m	(long lived isotope)	$1\ 10^{13}$
Tb-156m	(short lived isotope)	$4\ 10^{12}$
Tb-157		$1\ 10^{13}$
Tb-158		$2\ 10^{11}$
Tb-160		$5\ 10^{11}$
Tb-161		$2\ 10^{12}$
Thallium		
Tl-194		$1\ 10^{13}$
Tl-194m		$2\ 10^{12}$
Tl-195		$4\ 10^{12}$
Tl-197		$5\ 10^{12}$
Tl-198		$7\ 10^{12}$
Tl-198m		$2\ 10^{12}$
Tl-199		$6\ 10^{12}$
Tl-200		$1\ 10^{13}$
Tl-201		$7\ 10^{12}$
Tl-202		$7\ 10^{12}$
Tl-204		$2\ 10^{12}$
Thorium		
Th-226		$4\ 10^{11}$
Th-227		$2\ 10^{9}$
Th-228		$6\ 10^{8}$
Th-229		$1\ 10^{8}$
Th-230		$2\ 10^{8}$
Th-231		$2\ 10^{12}$
Th-232		$2\ 10^{8}$
Th-234		$3\ 10^{12}$
Thulium		
Tm-162		$2\ 10^{12}$
Tm-166		$3\ 10^{12}$
Tm-167		$4\ 10^{12}$
Tm-170		$2\ 10^{12}$
Tm-171		$1\ 10^{13}$
Tm-172		$2\ 10^{12}$
Tm-173		$2\ 10^{12}$
Tm-175		$2\ 10^{12}$

Radionuclide name, symbol	Radionuclide form	Quantity (Bq)
Tin		
Sn-110		$6\ 10^{13}$
Sn-111		$2\ 10^{12}$
Sn-113		$5\ 10^{12}$
Sn-117m		$3\ 10^{12}$
Sn-119m		$5\ 10^{12}$
Sn-121		$3\ 10^{12}$
Sn-121m		$4\ 10^{12}$
Sn-123		$2\ 10^{12}$
Sn-123m		$2\ 10^{12}$
Sn-125		$1\ 10^{12}$
Sn-126		$5\ 10^{11}$
Sn-127		$2\ 10^{12}$
Sn-128		$2\ 10^{12}$
Titanium		
Ti-44		$2\ 10^{11}$
Ti-45		$2\ 10^{12}$
Tungsten		
W-176		$5\ 10^{12}$
W-177		$3\ 10^{12}$
W-178		$6\ 10^{13}$
W-179		$1\ 10^{13}$
W-181		$1\ 10^{13}$
W-185		$4\ 10^{12}$
W-187		$2\ 10^{12}$
W-188		$3\ 10^{12}$
Uranium		
U-230		$2\ 10^{9}$
U-231		$7\ 10^{12}$
U-232		$6\ 10^{8}$
U-233		$3\ 10^{9}$
U-234		$3\ 10^{9}$
U-235		$3\ 10^{9}$
U-236		$3\ 10^{9}$
U-237		$2\ 10^{12}$
U-238		$3\ 10^{9}$
U-239		$2\ 10^{12}$
U-240		$2\ 10^{12}$
Vanadium		
V-47		$1\ 10^{12}$
V-48		$1\ 10^{12}$
V-49		$2\ 10^{14}$
Xenon		
Xe-120	(gas)	$1\ 10^{14}$
Xe-121	(gas)	$3\ 10^{13}$
Xe-122	(gas)	$1\ 10^{15}$
Xe-123	(gas)	$9\ 10^{13}$
Xe-125	(gas)	$2\ 10^{14}$
Xe-127	(gas)	$2\ 10^{14}$
Xe-129m	(gas)	$2\ 10^{15}$
Xe-131m	(gas)	$4\ 10^{15}$
Xe-133	(gas)	$1\ 10^{15}$
Xe-133m	(gas)	$2\ 10^{15}$
Xe-135	(gas)	$2\ 10^{14}$
Xe-135m	(gas)	$1\ 10^{14}$
Xe-138	(gas)	$5\ 10^{13}$

Radionuclide name, symbol	Radionuclide form	Quantity (Bq)
Ytterbium		
Yb-162		$1\ 10^{13}$
Yb-166		$8\ 10^{12}$
Yb-167		$4\ 10^{12}$
Yb-169		$3\ 10^{12}$
Yb-175		$4\ 10^{12}$
Yb-177		$2\ 10^{12}$
Yb-178		$2\ 10^{12}$
Yttrium		
Y-86		$2\ 10^{12}$
Y-86m		$1\ 10^{13}$
Y-87		$2\ 10^{13}$
Y-88		$2\ 10^{11}$
Y-90		$2\ 10^{12}$
Y-90m		$7\ 10^{12}$
Y-91		$2\ 10^{12}$
Y-91m		$2\ 10^{13}$
Y-92		$6\ 10^{11}$
Y-93		$8\ 10^{11}$
Y-94		$6\ 10^{11}$
Y-95		$6\ 10^{11}$
Zinc		
Zn-62		$1\ 10^{13}$
Zn-63		$1\ 10^{12}$
Zn-65		$5\ 10^{10}$
Zn-69		$2\ 10^{12}$
Zn-69m		$2\ 10^{13}$
Zn-71m		$2\ 10^{12}$
Zn-72		$3\ 10^{12}$
Zirconium		
Zr-86		$2\ 10^{13}$
Zr-88		$1\ 10^{12}$
Zr-89		$4\ 10^{12}$
Zr-93		$8\ 10^{11}$
Zr-95		$8\ 10^{11}$
Zr-97		$2\ 10^{12}$
Other radionuclides not listed above (see note)		$4\ 10^{7}$

Note: In the case of radionuclides not specified elsewhere in this Part, the quantity specified in this entry is to be used unless the Executive has approved some other quantity for that radionuclide.

461 The quantities of radionuclides are derived from a research project by the NRPB (see NRPB report NRPB-M1311 *Calculations to assist in the revision of IRR-85 with respect to Special Hazard Assessments (REPPIR Schedule 2)*).[25]

Part II

Quantity ratios for more than one radionuclide

1   For the purpose of regulation 3(2), the quantity ratio for more than one radionuclide is the sum of the quotients of the quantity of a radionuclide present Q_p divided by the quantity of that radionuclide specified in the appropriate column of Part I of this Schedule Q_{lim}, namely -

$$\sum \frac{Q_p}{Q_{lim}}$$

2   In any case where the isotopic composition of a radioactive substance is not known or is only partially known, the quantity ratio for that substance shall be calculated by using the values specified in the appropriate column in Part I for 'other radionuclides not listed above' for any radionuclide that has not been identified or where the quantity of a radionuclide is uncertain, unless the employer can show that the use of some other value is appropriate in the circumstances of a particular case, when he may use that value.

Masses of fissile material

Regulation 3(1)

For the purpose of regulation 3(1), the specified mass of a fissile material shall be -

(a)	plutonium as Pu 239 or Pu 241 or as a mixture of plutonium isotopes containing Pu 239 or Pu 241 -	150 grams;
(b)	uranium as U 233 -	150 grams;
(c)	uranium enriched in U 235 to more than 1% but not more than 5% -	500 grams;
(d)	uranium enriched in U 235 to more than 5% -	250 grams.

462   The masses relate to the potential for criticality of the fissile material.

Specified quantities for the transport of radionuclides

Regulation 3(1) and (3)

PART I

Table of radionuclides

Radionuclide name, symbol	Radionuclide form	Quantity (Bq)
Actinium		
Ac-225	(see note 1)	$6 \ 10^9$
Ac-227	(see note 1)	$9 \ 10^7$
Ac-228		$5 \ 10^{11}$
Aluminium		
Al-26		$1 \ 10^{11}$
Americium		
Am-241		$1 \ 10^9$
Am-242m	(see note 1)	$1 \ 10^9$
Am-243	(see note 1)	$1 \ 10^9$
Antimony		
Sb-122		$4 \ 10^{11}$
Sb-124		$6 \ 10^{11}$
Sb-125		$1 \ 10^{12}$
Sb-126		$4 \ 10^{11}$
Argon		
Ar-37		$4 \ 10^{13}$
Ar-39		$2 \ 10^{13}$
Ar-41		$3 \ 10^{11}$
Arsenic		
As-72		$3 \ 10^{11}$
As-73		$4 \ 10^{13}$
As-74		$9 \ 10^{11}$
As-76		$3 \ 10^{11}$
As-77		$7 \ 10^{11}$
Astatine		
At-211	(see note 1)	$5 \ 10^{11}$
Barium		
Ba-131	(see note 1)	$2 \ 10^{12}$
Ba-133		$3 \ 10^{12}$
Ba-133m		$6 \ 10^{11}$
Ba-140	(see note 1)	$3 \ 10^{11}$
Berkelium		
Bk-247		$8 \ 10^8$
Bk-249	(see note 1)	$3 \ 10^{11}$
Beryllium		
Be-7		$2 \ 10^{13}$
Be-10		$6 \ 10^{11}$

Radionuclide name, symbol	Radionuclide form	Quantity (Bq)
Bismuth		
Bi-205		$7 \ 10^{11}$
Bi-206		$3 \ 10^{11}$
Bi-207		$7 \ 10^{11}$
Bi-210		$6 \ 10^{11}$
Bi-210m	(see note 1)	$2 \ 10^{10}$
Bi-212	(see note 1)	$6 \ 10^{11}$
Bromine		
Br-76		$4 \ 10^{11}$
Br-77		$3 \ 10^{12}$
Br-82		$4 \ 10^{11}$
Cadmium		
Cd-109		$2 \ 10^{12}$
Cd-113m		$5 \ 10^{11}$
Cd-115	(see note 1)	$4 \ 10^{11}$
Cd-115m		$5 \ 10^{11}$
Caesium		
Cs-129		$4 \ 10^{12}$
Cs-131		$3 \ 10^{13}$
Cs-132		$1 \ 10^{12}$
Cs-134		$7 \ 10^{11}$
Cs-134m		$6 \ 10^{11}$
Cs-135		$1 \ 10^{12}$
Cs-136		$5 \ 10^{11}$
Cs-137	(see note 1)	$6 \ 10^{11}$
Calcium		
Ca-41		unlimited
Ca-45		$1 \ 10^{12}$
Ca-47	(see note 1)	$3 \ 10^{11}$
Californium		
Cf-248		$6 \ 10^{9}$
Cf-249		$8 \ 10^{8}$
Cf-250		$2 \ 10^{9}$
Cf-251		$7 \ 10^{8}$
Cf-252		$3 \ 10^{9}$
Cf-253	(see note 1)	$4 \ 10^{10}$
Cf-254		$1 \ 10^{9}$
Carbon		
C-11		$6 \ 10^{11}$
C-14		$3 \ 10^{12}$
Cerium		
Ce-139		$2 \ 10^{12}$
Ce-141		$6 \ 10^{11}$
Ce-143		$6 \ 10^{11}$
Ce-144	(see note 1)	$2 \ 10^{11}$
Chlorine		
Cl-36		$6 \ 10^{11}$
Cl-38		$2 \ 10^{11}$
Chromium		
Cr-51		$3 \ 10^{13}$

Radionuclide name, symbol	Radionuclide form	Quantity (Bq)
Cobalt		
Co-55		$5\ 10^{11}$
Co-56		$3\ 10^{11}$
Co-57		$1\ 10^{13}$
Co-58		$1\ 10^{12}$
Co-58m		$4\ 10^{13}$
Co-60		$4\ 10^{11}$
Copper		
Cu-64		$1\ 10^{12}$
Cu-67		$7\ 10^{11}$
Curium		
Cm-240		$2\ 10^{10}$
Cm-241		$1\ 10^{12}$
Cm-242		$1\ 10^{10}$
Cm-243		$1\ 10^{9}$
Cm-244		$2\ 10^{9}$
Cm-245		$9\ 10^{8}$
Cm-246		$9\ 10^{8}$
Cm-247	(see note 1)	$1\ 10^{9}$
Cm-248		$3\ 10^{8}$
Dysprosium		
Dy-159		$2\ 10^{13}$
Dy-165		$6\ 10^{11}$
Dy-166	(see note 1)	$3\ 10^{11}$
Erbium		
Er-169		$1\ 10^{12}$
Er-171		$5\ 10^{11}$
Europium		
Eu-147		$2\ 10^{12}$
Eu-148		$5\ 10^{11}$
Eu-149		$2\ 10^{13}$
Eu-150	(long lived isotope)	$7\ 10^{11}$
Eu-150	(short lived isotope)	$7\ 10^{11}$
Eu-152		$1\ 10^{12}$
Eu-152m		$8\ 10^{11}$
Eu-154		$6\ 10^{11}$
Eu-155		$3\ 10^{12}$
Eu-156		$7\ 10^{11}$
Fluorine		
F-18		$6\ 10^{11}$
Gadolinium	(see note 1)	
Gd-146		$5\ 10^{11}$
Gd-148		$2\ 10^{9}$
Gd-153		$9\ 10^{12}$
Gd-159		$6\ 10^{11}$
Gallium		
Ga-67		$3\ 10^{12}$
Ga-68		$5\ 10^{11}$
Ga-72		$4\ 10^{11}$

Radionuclide name, symbol	Radionuclide form	Quantity (Bq)
Germanium		
Ge-68	(see note 1)	$5 \ 10^{11}$
Ge-71		$4 \ 10^{13}$
Ge-77		$3 \ 10^{11}$
Gold		
Au-193		$2 \ 10^{12}$
Au-194		$1 \ 10^{12}$
Au-195		$6 \ 10^{12}$
Au-198		$6 \ 10^{11}$
Au-199		$6 \ 10^{11}$
Hafnium		
Hf-172	(see note 1)	$6 \ 10^{11}$
Hf-175		$3 \ 10^{12}$
Hf-181		$5 \ 10^{11}$
Hf-182		unlimited
Holmium		
Ho-166		$4 \ 10^{11}$
Ho-166m		$5 \ 10^{11}$
Hydrogen		
H-3		$4 \ 10^{13}$
Indium		
In-111		$3 \ 10^{12}$
In-113m		$2 \ 10^{12}$
In-114m	(see note 1)	$5 \ 10^{11}$
In-115m		$1 \ 10^{12}$
Iodine		
I-123		$3 \ 10^{12}$
I-124		$1 \ 10^{12}$
I-125		$3 \ 10^{12}$
I-126		$1 \ 10^{12}$
I-129		unlimited
I-131		$7 \ 10^{11}$
I-132		$4 \ 10^{11}$
I-133		$6 \ 10^{11}$
I-134		$3 \ 10^{11}$
I-135	(see note 1)	$6 \ 10^{11}$
Iridium		
Ir-189	(see note 1)	$1 \ 10^{13}$
Ir-190		$7 \ 10^{11}$
Ir-192		$6 \ 10^{11}$
Ir-194		$3 \ 10^{11}$
Iron		
Fe-52	(see note 1)	$3 \ 10^{11}$
Fe-55		$4 \ 10^{13}$
Fe-59		$9 \ 10^{11}$
Fe-60	(see note 1)	$2 \ 10^{11}$
Krypton		
Kr-81		$4 \ 10^{13}$
Kr-85		$1 \ 10^{13}$
Kr-85m		$3 \ 10^{12}$
Kr-87		$2 \ 10^{11}$

Radionuclide name, symbol	Radionuclide form	Quantity (Bq)
Lanthanum		
La-137		$6 \ 10^{12}$
La-140		$4 \ 10^{11}$
Lead		
Pb-201		$1 \ 10^{12}$
Pb-202		$2 \ 10^{13}$
Pb-203		$3 \ 10^{12}$
Pb-205		unlimited
Pb-210	(see note 1)	$5 \ 10^{10}$
Pb-212	(see note 1)	$2 \ 10^{11}$
Lutetium		
Lu-172		$6 \ 10^{11}$
Lu-173		$8 \ 10^{12}$
Lu-174		$9 \ 10^{12}$
Lu-174m		$1 \ 10^{13}$
Lu-177		$7 \ 10^{11}$
Magnesium		
Mg-28	(see note 1)	$3 \ 10^{11}$
Manganese		
Mn-52		$3 \ 10^{11}$
Mn-53		unlimited
Mn-54		$1 \ 10^{12}$
Mn-56		$3 \ 10^{11}$
Mercury		
Hg-194	(see note 1)	$1 \ 10^{12}$
Hg-195m	(see note 1)	$7 \ 10^{11}$
Hg-197		$1 \ 10^{13}$
Hg-197m		$4 \ 10^{11}$
Hg-203		$1 \ 10^{12}$
Molybdenum		
Mo-93		$2 \ 10^{13}$
Mo-99	(see note 1)	$6 \ 10^{11}$
Neodymium		
Nd-147		$6 \ 10^{11}$
Nd-149		$5 \ 10^{11}$
Neptunium		
Np-235		$4 \ 10^{13}$
Np-236	(long lived isotope)	$2 \ 10^{10}$
Np-236	(short lived isotope)	$2 \ 10^{12}$
Np-237		$2 \ 10^{9}$
Np-239		$4 \ 10^{11}$
Nickel		
Ni-59		unlimited
Ni-63		$3 \ 10^{13}$
Ni-65		$4 \ 10^{11}$
Niobium		
Nb-93m		$3 \ 10^{13}$
Nb-94		$7 \ 10^{11}$
Nb-95		$1 \ 10^{12}$
Nb-97		$6 \ 10^{11}$

Radionuclide name, symbol	Radionuclide form	Quantity (Bq)
Nitrogen N-13		$6\ 10^{11}$
Osmium Os-185 Os-191 Os-191m Os-193 Os-194	(see note 1)	$1\ 10^{12}$ $2\ 10^{12}$ $3\ 10^{13}$ $6\ 10^{11}$ $3\ 10^{11}$
Palladium Pd-103 Pd-107 Pd-109	(see note 1)	$4\ 10^{13}$ unlimited $5\ 10^{11}$
Phosphorus P-32 P-33		$5\ 10^{11}$ $1\ 10^{12}$
Platinum Pt-188 Pt-191 Pt-193 Pt-193m Pt-195m Pt-197 Pt-197m	(see note 1)	$8\ 10^{11}$ $3\ 10^{12}$ $4\ 10^{13}$ $5\ 10^{11}$ $5\ 10^{11}$ $6\ 10^{11}$ $6\ 10^{11}$
Plutonium Pu-236 Pu-237 Pu-238 Pu-239 Pu-240 Pu-241 Pu-242 Pu-244	(see note 1) (see note 1)	$3\ 10^{9}$ $2\ 10^{13}$ $1\ 10^{9}$ $1\ 10^{9}$ $1\ 10^{9}$ $6\ 10^{10}$ $1\ 10^{9}$ $1\ 10^{9}$
Polonium Po-210		$2\ 10^{10}$
Potassium K-40 K-42 K-43		$9\ 10^{11}$ $2\ 10^{11}$ $6\ 10^{11}$
Praseodymium Pr-142 Pr-143		$4\ 10^{11}$ $6\ 10^{11}$
Promethium Pm-143 Pm-144 Pm-145 Pm-147 Pm-148m Pm-149 Pm-151	(see note 1)	$3\ 10^{12}$ $7\ 10^{11}$ $1\ 10^{13}$ $2\ 10^{12}$ $7\ 10^{11}$ $6\ 10^{11}$ $6\ 10^{11}$

Radionuclide name, symbol	Radionuclide form	Quantity (Bq)
Protactinium Pa-230	(see note 1)	$7 \ 10^{10}$
Pa-231		$4 \ 10^{8}$
Pa-233		$7 \ 10^{11}$
Radium Ra-223	(see note 1)	$7 \ 10^{9}$
Ra-224	(see note 1)	$2 \ 10^{10}$
Ra-225	(see note 1)	$4 \ 10^{9}$
Ra-226	(see note 1)	$3 \ 10^{9}$
Ra-228	(see note 1)	$2 \ 10^{10}$
Radon Rn-222	(see note 1)	$4 \ 10^{9}$
Rhenium Re-184		$1 \ 10^{12}$
Re-184m		$1 \ 10^{12}$
Re-186		$6 \ 10^{11}$
Re-187		unlimited
Re-188		$4 \ 10^{11}$
Re-189	(see note 1)	$6 \ 10^{11}$
Re-natural		unlimited
Rhodium Rh-99		$2 \ 10^{12}$
Rh-101		$3 \ 10^{12}$
Rh-102		$5 \ 10^{11}$
Rh-102m		$2 \ 10^{12}$
Rh-103m		$4 \ 10^{13}$
Rh-105		$8 \ 10^{11}$
Rubidium Rb-81		$8 \ 10^{11}$
Rb-83	(see note 1)	$2 \ 10^{12}$
Rb-84		$1 \ 10^{12}$
Rb-86		$5 \ 10^{11}$
Rb-87		unlimited
Rb-natural		unlimited
Ruthenium Ru-97		$5 \ 10^{12}$
Ru-103	(see note 1)	$2 \ 10^{12}$
Ru-105		$6 \ 10^{11}$
Ru-106	(see note 1)	$2 \ 10^{11}$
Samarium Sm-145		$1 \ 10^{13}$
Sm-147		unlimited
Sm-151		$1 \ 10^{13}$
Sm-153		$6 \ 10^{11}$
Scandium Sc-44		$5 \ 10^{11}$
Sc-46		$5 \ 10^{11}$
Sc-47		$7 \ 10^{11}$
Sc-48		$3 \ 10^{11}$

Radionuclide name, symbol	Radionuclide form	Quantity (Bq)
Selenium		
Se-75		$3 \ 10^{12}$
Se-79		$2 \ 10^{12}$
Silicon		
Si-31		$6 \ 10^{11}$
Si-32		$5 \ 10^{11}$
Silver		
Ag-105		$2 \ 10^{12}$
Ag-108m	(see note 1)	$7 \ 10^{11}$
Ag-110m	(see note 1)	$4 \ 10^{11}$
Ag-111		$6 \ 10^{11}$
Sodium		
Na-22		$5 \ 10^{11}$
Na-24		$2 \ 10^{11}$
Strontium		
Sr-82	(see note 1)	$2 \ 10^{11}$
Sr-85		$2 \ 10^{12}$
Sr-85m		$5 \ 10^{12}$
Sr-87m		$3 \ 10^{12}$
Sr-89		$6 \ 10^{11}$
Sr-90	(see note 1)	$3 \ 10^{11}$
Sr-91	(see note 1)	$3 \ 10^{11}$
Sr-92	(see note 1)	$3 \ 10^{11}$
Sulphur		
S-35		$3 \ 10^{12}$
Tantalum		
Ta-178	(long lived isotope)	$8 \ 10^{11}$
Ta-179		$3 \ 10^{13}$
Ta-182		$5 \ 10^{11}$
Technetium		
Tc-95m	(see note 1)	$2 \ 10^{12}$
Tc-96		$4 \ 10^{11}$
Tc-96m	(see note 1)	$4 \ 10^{11}$
Tc-97		unlimited
Tc-97m		$1 \ 10^{12}$
Tc-98		$7 \ 10^{11}$
Tc-99		$9 \ 10^{11}$
Tc-99m		$4 \ 10^{12}$
Tellurium		
Te-121		$2 \ 10^{12}$
Te-121m		$3 \ 10^{12}$
Te-123m		$1 \ 10^{12}$
Te-125m		$9 \ 10^{11}$
Te-127		$7 \ 10^{11}$
Te-127m	(see note 1)	$5 \ 10^{11}$
Te-129		$6 \ 10^{11}$
Te-129m	(see note 1)	$4 \ 10^{11}$
Te-131m	(see note 1)	$5 \ 10^{11}$
Te-132	(see note 1)	$4 \ 10^{11}$

Radionuclide name, symbol	Radionuclide form	Quantity (Bq)
Terbium		
Tb-157		$4\ 10^{13}$
Tb-158		$1\ 10^{12}$
Tb-160		$6\ 10^{11}$
Thallium		
Tl-200		$9\ 10^{11}$
Tl-201		$4\ 10^{12}$
Tl-202		$2\ 10^{12}$
Tl-204		$7\ 10^{11}$
Thorium		
Th-227		$5\ 10^{9}$
Th-228	(see note 1)	$1\ 10^{9}$
Th-229		$5\ 10^{8}$
Th-230		$1\ 10^{9}$
Th-231		$2\ 10^{10}$
Th-232		unlimited
Th-234	(see note 1)	$3\ 10^{11}$
Th-natural		unlimited
Thulium		
Tm-167		$8\ 10^{11}$
Tm-170		$6\ 10^{11}$
Tm-171		$4\ 10^{13}$
Tin		
Sn-113	(see note 1)	$2\ 10^{12}$
Sn-117m		$4\ 10^{11}$
Sn-119m		$3\ 10^{13}$
Sn-121m	(see note 1)	$9\ 10^{11}$
Sn-123		$6\ 10^{11}$
Sn-125		$4\ 10^{11}$
Sn-126	(see note 1)	$4\ 10^{11}$
Titanium		
Ti-44	(see note 1)	$4\ 10^{11}$
Tungsten		
W-178	(see note 1)	$5\ 10^{12}$
W-181		$3\ 10^{13}$
W-185		$8\ 10^{11}$
W-187		$6\ 10^{11}$
W-188	(see note 1)	$3\ 10^{11}$

Radionuclide name, symbol	Radionuclide form	Quantity (Bq)
Uranium		
U-230	(fast lung absorption, see notes 1 and 2)	$1 \ 10^{11}$
U-230	(medium lung absorption, see notes 1 and 3)	$4 \ 10^{9}$
U-230	(slow lung absorption, see notes 1 and 4)	$3 \ 10^{9}$
U-232	(fast lung absorption, see note 2)	$1 \ 10^{10}$
U-232	(medium lung absorption, see note 3)	$7 \ 10^{9}$
U-232	(slow lung absorption, see note 4)	$1 \ 10^{9}$
U-233	(fast lung absorption, see note 2)	$9 \ 10^{10}$
U-233	(medium lung absorption, see note 3)	$2 \ 10^{10}$
U-233	(slow lung absorption, see note 4)	$6 \ 10^{9}$
U-234	(fast lung absorption, see note 2)	$9 \ 10^{10}$
U-234		$2 \ 10^{10}$
U-234	(medium lung absorption, see note 3)	$6 \ 10^{9}$
U-235	(slow lung absorption, see note 4)	unlimited
U-236	(all lung absorption types, see notes 1, 2, 3 and 4)	unlimited
U-236	(fast lung absorption, see note 2)	$2 \ 10^{10}$
U-236	(medium lung absorption, see note 3)	$6 \ 10^{9}$
U-238	(slow lung absorption, see note 4)	unlimited
U-natural	(all lung absorption types, see notes 2, 3 and 4)	unlimited
U (enriched to 20% or less)		unlimited
U-depleted	(see note 5)	unlimited
Vanadium		
V-48		$4 \ 10^{11}$
V-49		$4 \ 10^{13}$
Xenon		
Xe-122	(see note 1)	$4 \ 10^{11}$
Xe-123		$7 \ 10^{11}$
Xe-127		$2 \ 10^{12}$
Xe-131m		$4 \ 10^{13}$
Xe-133		$1 \ 10^{13}$
Xe-135		$2 \ 10^{12}$
Ytterbium		
Yb-169		$1 \ 10^{12}$
Yb-175		$9 \ 10^{11}$

Radionuclide name, symbol	Radionuclide form	Quantity (Bq)
Yttrium		
Y-87	(see note 1)	$1 \ 10^{12}$
Y-88		$4 \ 10^{11}$
Y-90		$3 \ 10^{11}$
Y-91		$6 \ 10^{11}$
Y-91m		$2 \ 10^{12}$
Y-92		$2 \ 10^{11}$
Y-93		$3 \ 10^{11}$
Zinc		
Zn-65		$2 \ 10^{12}$
Zn-69		$6 \ 10^{11}$
Zn-69m	(see note 1)	$6 \ 10^{11}$
Zirconium		
Zr-88		$3 \ 10^{12}$
Zr-93		unlimited
Zr-95	(see note 1)	$8 \ 10^{11}$
Zr-97	(see note 1)	$4 \ 10^{11}$
Other radionuclides not listed above where only beta or gamma emitting nuclides are known to be present	(see note 6)	$2 \ 10^{10}$
Other radionuclides not listed above where alpha emitting nuclides are known to be present or no relevant data are available	(see note 6)	$9 \ 10^{7}$

Note 1: Values include contributions from daughter nuclides with half-lives less than 10 days.

Note 2: These values apply only to compounds of uranium that take the chemical form of UF_6, UO_2F_2 and $UO_2(NO_3)_2$ in both normal and accident conditions of transport.

Note 3: These values apply only to compounds of uranium that take the chemical form of UO_3, UF_4, UCl_4 and hexavalent compounds, other than those specified in Note 2 above, in both normal and accident conditions of transport.

Note 4: These values apply to all compounds of uranium other than those specified in Notes 2 and 3 above.

*Note 5: These values apply to **unirradiated uranium** only.*

Note 6: In the case of radionuclides not specified elsewhere in this Part, the quantity specified in this entry is to be used unless the Executive has approved some other quantity for that radionuclide.

463 The quantities of radionuclides are those for Type A packages containing radioactive material in non-special form in the International Atomic Energy Agency's IAEA TS-R-1[26] (revision of ST-1 1996).

PART II

Quantity ratios for more than one radionuclide

1   For the purpose of regulation 3(3), the quantity ratio for more than one radionuclide is the sum of the quotients of the quantity of a radionuclide present Q_p divided by the quantity of that radionuclide specified in the appropriate column of Part I of this Schedule Q_{lim}, namely -

$$\sum \frac{Q_p}{Q_{lim}}$$

2   *In any case where the isotopic composition of a radioactive substance is not known or is only partially known, the quantity ratio for that substance shall be calculated by using the values specified in the appropriate column in Part I for 'other radionuclides not listed above' for any radionuclide that has not been identified or where the quantity of a radionuclide is uncertain, unless the employer can show that the use of some other value is appropriate in the circumstances of a particular case, when he may use that value.*

Schedule 5

Particulars to be included in an assessment report

Regulation 6(4)

The following particulars are required to be included in an assessment report under regulation 6(4) -

(a)   *the name and address of the operator or carrier;*

(b)   *the postal address of the premises where the radioactive substance will be processed, manufactured, used or stored, or where the facilities for processing, manufacture, use or storage exist or, in the case of transport, the postal address of the transport undertaking;*

(c)   *the date on which it is anticipated that the work with ionising radiation will commence or, if it has already commenced, a statement to that effect;*

(d)   *a general description of the premises or place including the geographical location, meteorological, geological, hydrographic conditions and, where material, the history of the premises, except that in the case of transport a general description shall be given of either -*

   (i)   *the starting and end points of the journeys and transhipment points, or*

   (ii)   *the criteria to be used for route selection;*

(e)   *in the case of an assessment by an operator, a description of any radioactive substance on the premises which is likely to exceed any quantity or mass specified in Schedule 2 or Schedule 3, as the case may be, which description shall where practicable include details of the radionuclides present and their likely maximum quantities;*

(f)   *in the case of an assessment by a carrier, a description of any radioactive substance which is likely to exceed any quantity or mass specified in Schedule 4 or Schedule 3, as the case may be, which description shall where practicable include details of the radionuclides present and their likely maximum quantities;*

(g)   *except in the case of an assessment relating to transport, a plan of the premises in question and a map of the environs to a scale large enough to enable the premises and any features which could affect the general risk in an emergency to be identified;*

(h)   *a diagram and description of any single plant or enclosed system containing more than the quantity or mass of any radioactive substance specified in Schedule 2 or Schedule 3, as the case may be, or, in the case of the transport of more than the quantity or mass of any radioactive substance specified in Schedule 4 or Schedule 3, as the case may be, the nature of the containment for the radioactive substance, the type of vehicle and the means of securing the load within or on the vehicle;*

(i) those factors which could precipitate a major release of any radioactive substance and the measures to be taken to prevent or control such release and information showing the maximum quantity of radioactive substance which, in the event of a major failure of containment, would be released to the atmosphere including, in respect of premises, the identification of plant and other activities anywhere on the premises which could precipitate such release;

(j) those factors which could precipitate a smaller but continuing release of any radioactive substance and the measures to be taken to prevent or control such releases to atmosphere;

(k) those factors which could give rise to an incident involving the initiation of an unintended self-sustaining nuclear chain reaction or the loss of control of an intended self-sustaining nuclear chain reaction and, in either case, the measures to be taken to prevent or control any such incident;

(l) information concerning the management systems and staffing arrangements by which the radioactive substance is controlled and by which the procedures are controlled;

(m) except in the case of an assessment relating to transport, information about the size and distribution of the population in the vicinity of premises to which the report relates;

(n) an assessment of the area which is likely to be affected by the dispersal of any radioactive substance as a result of any radiation emergency and the period of time over which such dispersal is likely to take place;

(o) an assessment of the likely exposures to ionising radiation of any person or class of persons as a result of any radiation emergency; and

(p) an assessment of the necessity for an emergency plan to be prepared by the operator or carrier.

464 When assessing the area likely to be affected by the dispersal of any radioactive substance (paragraph (n)), the assessment should take into account intervention levels specified for foods and animal feeds (see guidance to Schedule 8, Part II).

465 The assessment report should contain the details required from (a) to (p) as described. The information presented should be sufficient for HSE to be able to confirm the conclusions reached. The documentation should also have been subject to appropriate document control procedures before issue.
NB A different version of the assessment may be made available to the public - see the guidance paragraphs 420-427 to regulation 16(6).

Schedule 6

Further particulars that the Executive may require

Regulation 6(5)

A further assessment and report may be required under regulation 6(5) in respect of the following matters -

(a) the analysis carried out to establish the likely consequences of any hazard, including the likely doses of ionising radiation to which members of the *public might be exposed, and the probability of the occurrence of such hazard;*

(b)   *the number of persons whose health or safety might be affected by the hazard;*

(c)   *the management systems and staffing arrangements by which any hazard is to be or is controlled;*

(d)   *the safety systems, procedures and monitoring systems by which any hazard is to be or is controlled;*

(e)   *the qualifications, experience and training of staff concerned;*

(f)   *the design, construction, operation or maintenance of any equipment (including the incorporation of adequate safety or reliability features of such equipment) which is used for the purposes of intervention or which is used to control any hazard;*

(g)   *the design and operating documentation;*

(h)   *the design and operation of containment and pressure systems;*

(i)   *the protection of persons from the effects of loss of containment; and*

(j)   *the procedures for the reporting of and learning from radiation emergencies.*

466   The additional assessment would be expected to address uncertainties in the calculations carried out. Examples of issues to be covered include: uncertainties in the input data used; the range of uncertainty in the derivation of fault sequences; and identification of the potential for a sudden increase in risk. The significance of these factors should be assessed and reported. In particular, the consequence analysis should identify those members of the public who may be affected. The calculations should also confirm the probability of occurrence for such a hazard.

467   The additional assessment carried out would be expected to identify the number of people whose health and safety would be affected by the hazard - this information should be recorded. This is needed to ensure that the potential impact of any future proposed changes at or around the premises, such as additional developments, can be readily assessed and their impact evaluated.

468   There should be arrangements in place for controlling the hazard during a radiation emergency. These arrangements should be documented and would be expected to include: arrangements for controlling plant and equipment; management systems and staffing arrangements for responding to an emergency; documented procedures for implementing the emergency response and appropriate monitoring systems; and documentation containing the qualifications, training and experience of those staff who have responsibilities for responding to an emergency.

469   The arrangements for design, operation or maintenance of any equipment used for intervention or controlling the hazard should be identified and made available. The areas which should be considered are: design specifications for performance and reliability; operational limits and conditions appropriate for the hazard; and the frequency and extent of maintenance and testing requirements to demonstrate 'continued fitness for purpose'.

470 Design and operating documentation covering details of the operating regimes should be made available, including limits and conditions as well as reliability requirements of safety-related plant and equipment. Such information would also be expected for the design and operation of containment and pressure systems. Consideration should also be given to demonstrating that non-safety related equipment which could potentially affect safety-related plant and equipment had been considered and any potential impact assessed.

471 The arrangements for responding to a radiation emergency should be made available to enable HSE to determine how they would be implemented. This should include arrangements for reporting radiation emergencies and measures to incorporate 'lessons learned' from real events into the emergency plan or planning arrangements, as appropriate.

Schedule 7

Information to be included in emergency plans

Regulations 7(2), 8(2) and 9(2)

PART I

Information to be included in an operator's emergency plan

The information referred to in regulation 7(2) is as follows -

> (a) *the names or positions of persons authorised to set emergency procedures in motion and the person in charge of and co-ordinating the on-site mitigatory action;*

472 The plan should include the premises command structure for managing the on-site response in accordance with the planned scheme. There will be times when senior managers are not available and appropriate arrangements should be included for these circumstances. It is recommended that the names and telephone numbers of authorised personnel are included in the annexes of emergency plans; this will help with updating.

> (b) *the name or position of the person with responsibility for liaison with the local authority responsible for preparing the off-site emergency plan;*

473 This is normally the person with responsibility for the operator's emergency plan. It is recommended that the names and telephone numbers of authorised personnel are included in the annexes of emergency plans; this will help with updating.

> (c) *for reasonably foreseeable conditions or events which could be significant in bringing about a radiation emergency, a description of the action which should be taken to control the conditions or events and to limit their consequences, including a description of the safety equipment and the resources available;*

474 This is the principal component of the operator's emergency plan and should include:

(a) the events with the potential to cause a radiation emergency;

(b) the intended strategy for dealing with these events should they come about;

127

(c)   details of the personnel who have roles to play in the emergency response, and their responsibilities;

(d)   details of the availability and function of special emergency equipment including fire-fighting materials, and damage control and repair items; and

(e)   details of the availability and function of other resources.

(d)   the arrangements for limiting the risks to persons on the premises including how warnings are to be given and the actions persons are expected to take on receipt of a warning;

475   This should include the systems, equipment and facilities for early detection of a developing radiation emergency, and the responsibilities for initiating the suitable responses by the operator's personnel (to evacuate, shelter, use personal protective equipment etc).

(e)   the arrangements for providing early warning of the incident to the local authority responsible for setting the off-site emergency plan in motion, the type of information which should be contained in an initial warning and the arrangements for the provision of more detailed information as it becomes available;

476   This should include:

(a)   the operator's arrangements for alerting responding organisations (which by local agreement may be by a body acting on the operator's behalf, such as the police service) and when this should be done (see guidance paragraphs 314-320 on regulation 13); and

(b)   the type of information that they will require, before and during their response, in what form, to whom and by whom.

(f)   the arrangements for providing assistance with off-site mitigatory action; and

477   This should include, for example, details of:

(a)   any special equipment, expertise or facilities which can be used off-site; and

(b)   the role of the establishment's personnel in briefing the media including the use of media briefing facilities.

(g)   the arrangements for emergency exposures including the dose levels which have been determined as appropriate for the purposes of putting into effect the emergency plan.

478   This should include:

(a)   the liaison arrangements with other employers (for example emergency services) to reach agreement with the operator on the dose level(s) for the purposes of on-site (and off-site) mitigatory action;

(b)   the different scenarios (if appropriate) for different dose levels that may be required on-site, for example at the reactor building or at the site boundary (or off-site, for example at specified distances outside the site boundary).

PART II

Information to be included in a carrier's emergency plan

The information referred to in regulation 8(2) is as follows -

> *(a) the names or positions of persons authorised to set emergency procedures in motion and the person in charge of and co-ordinating the mitigatory action;*

479 The plan should include the command structure for managing the response at the scene of a rail transport accident causing, or likely to cause a radiation emergency. There will be times when senior managers are not available and appropriate arrangements should be included for these circumstances. It is recommended that the names and telephone numbers of authorised personnel are included in the annexes of emergency plans; this will help with updating.

> *(b) for reasonably foreseeable conditions or events which could be significant in bringing about a radiation emergency, a description of the action which should be taken to control the conditions or events and to limit their consequences, including a description of the safety equipment and the resources available;*

480 This is the principal component of the carrier's emergency plan and should include:

(a) the events with the potential to cause a radiation emergency;

(b) the intended strategy for dealing with these events should they come about;

(c) details of the personnel who have roles to play in the emergency response, and their responsibilities;

(d) details of the availability and function of special emergency equipment including fire-fighting materials, and damage control and repair items; and

(e) details of the availability and function of other resources.

> *(c) the arrangements for providing early warning of the incident, the type of information which should be contained in an initial warning and the arrangements for the provision of more detailed information as it becomes available; and*

481 This should include:

(a) the arrangements for alerting the emergency services and when this should be done (see guidance paragraphs 314-320 on regulation 13); and

(b) the type of information that they will require, before and during their response, in what form, to whom and by whom.

> *(d) the arrangements for emergency exposures including the dose levels which have been determined as appropriate for the purposes of putting into effect the emergency plan.*

482 This should include:

(a) the liaison arrangements with other employers (for example emergency services) to reach agreement with the carrier on the dose level(s) for the purposes of mitigatory action at the scene of the accident;

(b) the different scenarios (if appropriate) for different dose levels that may be required, for example at the site of the accident or at specified distances from the accident.

PART III

Information to be included in an off-site emergency plan

The information referred to in regulation 9(2) is as follows -

> *(a) the names or positions of persons authorised to set emergency procedures in motion and of persons authorised to take charge of and co-ordinate the off-site mitigatory action;*

483 This should include the management structure for organising and managing the off-site response in the event of a radiation emergency. The responding organisations should strive to work together as a team to maximise the effectiveness of the response to an emergency, and the response should be co-ordinated and have common basic objectives.

> *(b) the arrangements for receiving early warning of incidents, and alert and call-out procedures;*

484 This is primarily concerned with bringing the off-site emergency response into action. The off-site emergency plan should include details of:

(a) how a warning of a developing or actual radiation emergency will be received by the off-site emergency services; and

(b) how the warning will be cascaded, as necessary, to the other off-site agencies involved, or likely to be involved, in the response to an emergency (see guidance paragraphs 314-320 and 324-325 on regulation 13).

> *(c) the arrangements for co-ordinating resources necessary to implement the off-site emergency plan;*

485 Information should be included in the off-site emergency plan on how the resources identified in the response arrangements will be mobilised, and how the actions of the off-site organisations will be co-ordinated; this information should complement and support the information required in the previous paragraphs. The information should include:

(a) which organisations have a role to play in the emergency response, and their roles and responsibilities;

(b) how each organisation will be alerted and will go about putting their emergency arrangements into action;

(c) how the emergency intervention personnel from the premises and the emergency services will recognise each other at the scene;

(d) how the intervention personnel from the responding organisations and premises will communicate to obtain and transmit information needed for decision making, in accordance with their agreed roles and responsibilities;

(e) the location where the emergency services, intervention personnel from the premises and other relevant agencies will rendezvous off-site, if necessary; and

(f) how intervention personnel from the responding organisations will gain access to the premises, to any special equipment or to any other resources which may be required in the response.

(d) the arrangements for providing assistance with on-site mitigatory action;

486 This may, under many circumstances, mean the off-site fire service coming on to the premises and taking over full responsibility for dealing with the response to the radiation emergency. The following details should be included:

(a) the events identified with the potential to cause a radiation emergency;

(b) the intended strategy for dealing with these events on the premises should they come about;

(c) details of the personnel/organisations who have roles to play in the on-site response, and their responsibilities;

(d) arrangements for briefing intervention personnel arriving at the premises;

(e) details of the availability and function of special equipment including fire-fighting materials, damage control and repair items; and

(f) details of the availability and function of other resources.

(e) the arrangements for off-site mitigatory action;

487 This is about mitigating the off-site effects of radiation emergencies which may include:

(a) sheltering or evacuating members of the public;

(b) distributing 'stable iodine' tablets to members of the public;

(c) controlling traffic, for example maintaining essential emergency services' routes; and

(d) preventing people entering the affected area.

(f) the arrangements for providing the public with specific information relating to the emergency and the behaviour which it should adopt; and

488 The off-site emergency plan should include information on:

(a) how the public in the vicinity of the premises will be alerted in the event of a radiation emergency;

(b) how they will be told what they should do; and

(c)   how they will be told that the danger is passed and they may return to their normal activities.

489 This will refer to the prior information that will have been supplied to those in the vicinity of the premises (see regulation 16), and the supply of information to the public in the event of a radiation emergency (see regulation 17). The public may be warned by alarm, siren, telephone, loud hailer or some other system; this is for local agreement and recording in the emergency plan. The prior information should tell the public in the vicinity of the premises about the warning mechanism, for example the meanings of different alarms and sirens. It should be noted that prior warning is not always possible.

> (g)   *the arrangements for emergency exposures including the dose levels which have been determined as appropriate for the purposes of putting into effect the emergency plan.*

490 This should include:

(a)   the liaison arrangements with other employers (for example, emergency services) to reach agreement with the operator on the dose level(s) for the purposes of off-site (and on-site) mitigatory action;

(b)   the different scenarios (if appropriate) for different dose levels that may be required off-site, for example at specified distances outside the site boundary (or on-site, for example at the reactor building or at the site boundary).

Principles and purposes of intervention

Regulations 7(4) and (5), 8(5) and (6), and 9(10) and (11)

PART I

Principles to which emergency plans shall have regard

An emergency plan drawn up pursuant to regulation 7, 8 or 9 respectively shall, in so far as it applies to any radiation emergency, be drawn up having regard to the following principles -

> (a)   *the intervention shall be undertaken only if the reduction in the detriment due to the radiation resulting from the radiation emergency is sufficient to justify the harm and costs, including the social costs, of the intervention; and*

> (b)   *the form, scale and duration of the intervention shall be carried out in such a way as to ensure that exposures to radiation are kept as low as is reasonably practicable so that the benefit of the reduction in health detriment less the detriment associated with the intervention will be maximised.*

491 For guidance on principles, see guidance to regulations 7(4), 8(5) and 9(10), and guidance from the NRPB (*Documents of the NRPB*, 1(4)[19]).

PART II

Purposes of intervention

The purposes of intervention referred to in regulations 7(5), 8(6) and regulation 9(11) are -

(a) *reducing or stopping at source direct radiation and the emission of radionuclides;*

(b) *reducing the transfer of radioactive substances to individuals from the environment; and*

492 Emergency plans should address intervention levels specified for foods, drinking water and animal feeds.

493 Regulations from the Council of the European Communities specify intervention levels (here termed CFILs - Council Food Intervention Levels) for radioactive contamination in foods, drinking water and animal feeds. These CFILs will be legally binding on the UK following an accident. FSA holds principal responsibility for decisions on food safety advice and restriction orders following a radiation emergency. NRPB has provided guidance for CFILs' implementation in the UK. The relevant Regulations and NRPB guidance are:

(a) Council Regulation (Euratom) No. 3954/87 of 22 December 1987 laying down maximum permitted levels of radioactive contamination of foodstuffs and of feedingstuffs following a nuclear accident or any other case of radiological emergency *Official Journal of the European Communities* (1987) No L371, 11-13 amended by Council Regulation 2218/89 *Official Journal of the European Communities* (1989) **32**, No L211, 1-3.[35]

(b) Commission Regulation (Euratom) No. 944/89 of 12 April 1989 laying down maximum permitted levels of radioactive contamination in minor foodstuffs following a nuclear accident or any other case of radiological emergency *Official Journal of the European Communities* (1989) **32**, No L101, 17-18.[36]

(c) Commission Regulation (Euratom) No 770/90 of 29 March 1990 laying down maximum permitted levels of radioactive contamination of feedingstuffs following a nuclear accident or any other case of radiological emergency *Official Journal of the European Communities* (1990) No L833, 78-79.[37]

(d) NRPB guidance on restrictions on foods and water following a radiological accident. (*Documents of the NRPB*, 5(1)).[32]

(c) *reducing the exposure and organising the treatment of persons who have been subject to exposure to radiation.*

494 For further guidance on purposes of intervention, see guidance to regulations 7(5), 8(6) and 9(11).

Prior information to be supplied and made publicly available

Regulation 16(1)

495 The purpose of this Schedule is to set out the minimum items that the prior information required by regulation 16 should cover.

496 Prior information is intended to give local householders and others a sufficiently clear understanding of the actions that they may be asked to take in a radiation emergency, so that should such an event occur, the necessary

measures can be implemented smoothly and speedily. So, it is of paramount importance to draft and present the information with absolute clarity and in a way that creates understanding, not alarm. The use of maps and illustrations can be a particularly effective way of putting over some of this information.

497   Any final draft of an information booklet should be tested out on a group of people who have little understanding of the subject. Only after any deficiencies have been rectified should the booklet be printed.

498   There are other items of information which, though not prescribed, would be sensible to include in any such booklet. These are:

(a)   the area determined by HSE for prior information distribution, perhaps by use of a map;

(b)   what additional and more detailed information has been made publicly available and where it can be found; and

(c)   the date of publication of the booklet and the fact that it is valid for three years.

1   Basic facts about radioactivity and its effects on persons and on the environment.

499   The facts about radioactivity should introduce the reader to basic concepts, such as radiation dose, quantities and units. An explanation about natural radioactivity may also be helpful here. The explanation on the effects of radioactivity should highlight the difference between internal and external radiation, the exposure pathways for humans, including through contaminated food and drink, and the short- and long-term effects of exposure and how these are affected by the level of dose.

500   This information is not premises-specific or transport-specific and should not change significantly with time. So, it would be permissible for this purpose to use a suitable standard leaflet or booklet produced by another organisation. However, it should still be distributed at the same time as and associated with the other information.

2   The various types of radiation emergency covered and their consequences for the general public and the environment.

501   This should describe in terms comprehensible to the reader the work activity and event(s) which may give rise to a radiation emergency, and the likelihood of such an emergency occurring. How such emergencies can affect people and the environment (for example through dispersion and settling of radioactive dust) should then be explained. The role of the weather and particularly the effect of wind direction should also be explained in terms of its consequences for exposure and causing contamination, and how rapidly this would occur.

3   Emergency measures envisaged to alert, protect and assist the general public in the event of a radiation emergency.

502   This should specify how people will be initially alerted to the existence of a radiation emergency which might affect them. How they can continue to keep themselves informed on the development of events should also be stated. This is normally achieved by tuning to a local radio or television station with whom prior agreement has been reached to perform this role. (Such an agreement would form part of the arrangements that local authorities are required to prepare under regulation 17.)

Guidance
Schedule 9

503   There should then be a general description of the off-site or carrier's emergency plan in so far as they concern the protection of the public.

Schedule 9

4   Appropriate information on action to be taken by the general public in the event of a radiation emergency.

Guidance

504   This is the key part of the prior information which describes the action that people should take if a radiation emergency occurs and how each different action will work in terms of reducing radiation doses. It should cover such matters as:

(a)   sheltering and associated actions;

(b)   distribution and taking of 'stable iodine' tablets, where appropriate;

(c)   evacuation, how the advice is to be given, what actions to take before leaving, what to do with pets and other animals, what to take, how to go, where to go, what happens to children at school, what arrangements there are for the sick and elderly; and

Schedule 9

(d)   longer term advice on the consumption of contaminated food and drink.

Schedule 9

5   The authority or authorities responsible for implementing the emergency measures and action referred to in paragraphs 3 and 4 above.

Guidance
Schedule 9

505   The information provided in response to paragraphs 3 and 4 should make clear which authorities are responsible for implementing the various measures described.

Schedule 10

Information to be supplied in the event of a radiation emergency

Regulation 17(4)

Guidance

506   This Schedule lists information to be provided in the event of an actual radiation emergency through the arrangements established by local authorities under regulation 17. Regulation 17(4) makes clear that only information relevant to a particular type of radiation emergency needs to be supplied. Inclusion of information that is not relevant to the particular circumstances of the radiation emergency is likely to cause confusion and be counterproductive.

507   The information coverage will be similar in scope to that required for prior information but only in respect of the specific radiation emergency that has arisen. Where protective measures are referred to, regulation 17(4) requires the information to identify the authority or authorities responsible for implementing that measure.

508   Where information is supplied, the degree of detail will necessarily depend on the circumstances at the time. There could be some situations where an accident has happened and where a release of radioactivity is anticipated but has not yet occurred. This permits greater breadth and depth of information to be disseminated. In situations where speed of action is paramount, then the information will have to be kept to the bare minimum, at least initially. The different information requirements should be considered and planned for in the arrangements for their distribution when a radiation emergency occurs, or an event occurs which could reasonably be expected to lead to a radiation emergency.

Schedule 10

1   Information on the type of emergency which has occurred, and, where possible, its characteristics, for example, its origin, extent and probable development.

509   This would be much as provided under paragraph 2 of Schedule 9, but related to the specific emergency that has occurred, the conditions that actually exist and the likely course of development.

510   The description of the events in the International Atomic Energy Agency's International Nuclear Event Scale (INES)[38] can be used as a means of informing the public of the magnitude of any event.

2   Advice on health protection measures, which, depending on the type of emergency, might include -

(a)   any restrictions on the consumption of certain foodstuffs and water supply likely to be contaminated;

(b)   any basic rules on hygiene and decontamination;

(c)   any recommendation to stay indoors;

(d)   the distribution and use of protective substances;

(e)   any evacuation arrangements;

(f)   special warnings for certain population groups.

511   Similarly, this should be much as provided under paragraph 4 of Schedule 9, but related to the specific health protection measures relevant to the circumstances. Details concerning evacuation arrangements are especially important. The target audience of information in respect of sub-paragraph (a) could include providers of fresh food and water, for example farmers and water suppliers, as well as consumers. (See guidance on Schedule 8, Part II, paragraph (b), regarding food safety advice and restriction orders. See paragraph 438 on regulation 17(3) regarding informing the public about restrictions on consumption of water.)

3   Any announcements recommending co-operation with instructions or requests by the competent authorities.

512   Individuals cannot be compelled to co-operate with any health protection measures that have been decided on (such as evacuation), but any announcements should make clear that this is authoritative advice which it is in their interests to follow.

4   Where an occurrence which is likely to give rise to a release of radioactivity or ionising radiation has happened but no release has yet taken place, the information and advice should include the following -

(a)   an invitation to tune in to radio or television;

(b)   preparatory advice to establishments with particular collective responsibilities; and

(c)   recommendations to occupational groups particularly affected.

513   Where an accident does not lead immediately to a release of radioactivity, advantage should be taken of this pre-release period to:

(a) prepare people by getting them to tune in to local radio and television stations;

(b) alert and provide preparatory advice to establishments within the potentially affected area, such as schools, factories, commercial buildings, hospitals, general practices and nursing homes; and

(c) advise particular groups of people, such as children and pregnant women, regarding food and drink consumption, and farmers regarding their crops and livestock.

514 Also consider particular establishments as priority places for the receipt of information about an accident, including its magnitude, likely impact and guidance on the steps to be taken.

5 If time permits, information setting out the basic facts about radioactivity and its effects on persons and on the environment.

515 Under emergency circumstances, distribution of this background information cannot be a priority, but as time passes and if the pressure eases, this should be given attention. This information is the same as required by paragraph 1 of Schedule 9, and where a standard leaflet or booklet has been used for this purpose, this could be redistributed to those affected.

Amendment of Regulations

Regulation 21

The Fire Certificates (Special Premises) Regulations 1976

1 Paragraph 14 of Schedule 1 to the Fire Certificates (Special Premises) Regulations 1976[a] shall be deleted and the following substituted -

> *"14. Premises to which the Radiation (Emergency Preparedness and Public Information) Regulations 2001 apply by virtue of regulation 3 of those Regulations. "*

The Ionising Radiations Regulations 1999

2 The 1999 Regulations shall be amended in accordance with paragraphs 3 to 9.

3 In regulation 21(3)(i), the word "to" shall be inserted before "maintain".

4 In regulation 35(1), after the words "these Regulations" there shall be inserted the words "or of the Radiation (Emergency Preparedness and Public Information) Regulations 2001."

5 After regulation 35, there shall be inserted the following regulation -

"Enforcement

35A. Insofar as any provision of regulation 21 is made under section 2(2) of the European Communities Act 1972, sections -

(a) 16 to 21 (approval of codes of practice and enforcement);

(a) SI 1976/2003; the only relevant amending instrument is as amended by SI 1985/1333.

Figure 1 Sealed source dispersibility assessment flow chart

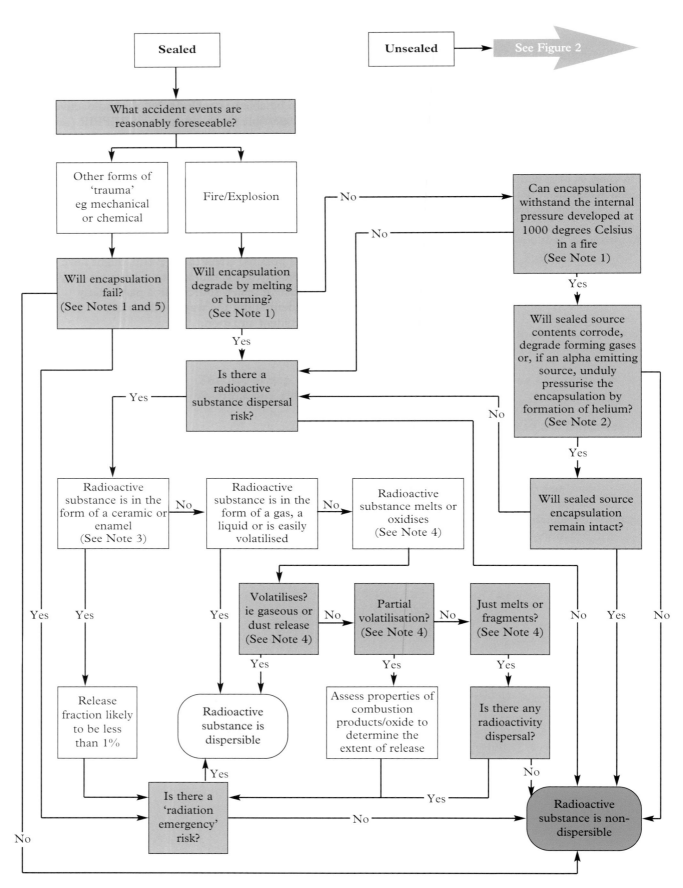

Figure 2 Unsealed source dispersibility assessment flow chart

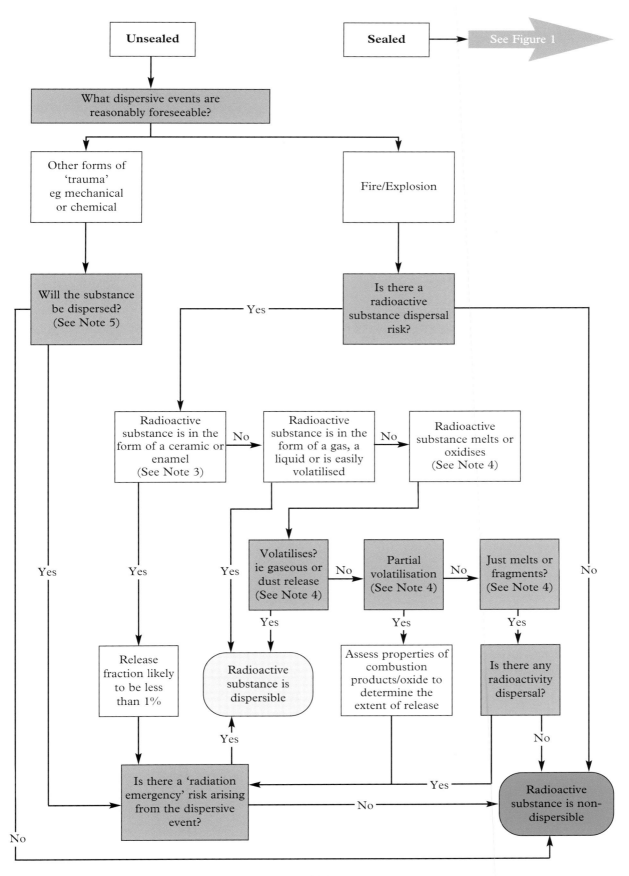

Notes to Figures 1 and 2

Note 1

Issues to consider are whether the radioactive substance is in the form of a sealed source whose fabrication is compliant with a recognised standard, and whether it is still within its recommended service life.

Two appropriate standards are ISO2919: 1999[40] or BS5288: 1976;[41] these use numerical class descriptors to specify performance characteristics. For more information about sealed source integrity specification, see *Release fractions for radioactive sources in fires.*[39]

Sealed source classification standards are essentially about encapsulation type specification. The ability of a particular sealed source to meet the encapsulation integrity assigned to it in accordance with a relevant standard will very much depend upon the quality control used during its manufacture, its service life history (ie whether it has ever been 'traumatised') and whether it is still within its manufacturer's recommended service life.

Note 2

Alpha sources 'release' helium over time, which may cause the encapsulation to become over-pressurised in the event of fire. Sealed source performance standards do take account of this phenomenon in their classification criteria. Operators who use these types of source should therefore seek advice from their manufacturer about the encapsulation failure risk in the event of accidents that cause encapsulation heating. Section 4 of *Release fractions for radioactive sources in fires* gives more information on this issue.

Note 3

Ceramic materials are extremely stable at high temperature and are therefore not easily volatilised; they remain solid up to approximately 700-1000°C, thereafter becoming increasingly soft and tacky as temperature is increased until, at around 1400°C, they start to melt.

The release fraction from a ceramic radioactive substance heated in a fire can be regarded as very low and will typically not exceed 1%.

Note 4

Section 5 of *Release fractions for radioactive sources in fires* gives information about how to assess release consequences in the event of radioactive substance oxidation.

Radioactive substances such as iridium metal and gadolinium oxide are particularly stable at high temperatures. If these materials are used in the form of implantable wires, for example in nuclear medicine applications, it is reasonable to assume that they are non-dispersible for the purpose of REPPIR.

Note 5

The kind of mechanical traumas operators will need to consider are those that might lead to radioactive substance dispersal, for example impaction, crushing and grinding of a solid radioactive substance or breakage of a storage vessel which contains a radioactive substance in the form of a liquid or powder. This type of event may lead to an increased fire risk if the radioactive substance is volatile and combustible or pyrophoric when present as an aerosol or dust cloud.

The objective of this aspect of the assessment process is to establish whether mechanical trauma scenarios have associated with them a risk of radiation emergency as defined in REPPIR.

Appendix 2

Acronyms

ACPO	Association of Chief Police Officers
ADMLC	Atmospheric Dispersion Modelling Liaison Committee
CAA	Civil Aviation Authority
CACFOA	Chief and Assistant Chief Fire Officers Association
CAP 168	Civil Aviation Publication 168 *Licensing of aerodromes*
CDGRR	Carriage of Dangerous Goods by Rail Regulations 1996
COMAH	Control of Major Accident Hazards Regulations 1999
COSLA	Convention of Scottish Local Authorities
DEFRA	Department for Environment, Food and Rural Affairs
DSHAR87	Dangerous Substances in Harbour Areas Regulations 1987
DTI	Department of Trade and Industry
DTLR	Department for Transport, Local Government and the Regions
EA	Environment Agency
EPS	Emergency Planning Society
ERLs	Emergency Reference Levels
FSA	Food Standards Agency
HAZAM	Hazard assessment methodology
HAZOP	Hazard operability analysis
HSE	Health and Safety Executive
IAEA	International Atomic Energy Authority
LGA	Local Government Association
MCA	Maritime and Coastguard Agency
MHSWR	Management of Health and Safety at Work Regulations 1999
MoD	Ministry of Defence
NEPLG	Nuclear Emergency Planning Liaison Group
NHS	National Health Service
NIA65	Nuclear Installations Act 1965
NRPB	National Radiological Protection Board
PIRER	Public Information for Radiation Emergencies Regulations 1992
REPPIR	Radiation (Emergency Preparedness and Public Information) Regulations 2001
RMTD	Radioactive Materials Transport Division
RSCR	Railway Safety Case Regulations 2000
SEHD	Scottish Executive Health Department
SEPA	Scottish Environment Protection Agency
'The 1974 Act'	Health and Safety at Work etc Act 1974
'The 1985 Regulations'	Ionising Radiations Regulations 1985
'The 1996 Regulations'	Packaging, Labelling and Carriage of Radioactive Materials by Rail Regulations 1996, as amended
'The 1999 Regulations'	Ionising Radiations Regulations 1999
'The BSS96 Directive'	Basic Safety Standards Directive 1996[2]

References

1   *Health and Safety at Work etc Act 1974 Ch 37* The Stationery Office 1974 ISBN 0 10 543774 3

2   Council Directive 96/29/Euratom of 13 May 1996 laying down basic safety standards for the protection of the health of workers and the general public against the dangers arising from ionising radiation *Official Journal of the European Communities* (1996) **39**, No L159, 1-114 ISBN 0 11 915263 0

3   *Work with ionising radiation. Ionising Radiations Regulations 1999. Approved Code of Practice and guidance* L121 HSE Books 2000 ISBN 0 7176 1746 7

4   *A guide to the Public Information for Radiation Emergencies Regulations 1992. Guidance on Regulations* L31 HSE Books 1992 ISBN 0 11 886350 9

5   Council Directive 89/618/Euratom of 27 November 1989 on informing the general public about health protection measures to be applied and steps to be taken in the event of a radiological emergency *Official Journal of the European Communities* (1989) **32**, No L357, 31-34

6   *A guide to the Control of Major Accident Hazard Regulations 1999 (COMAH). Guidance on Regulations* L111 HSE Books 1999 ISBN 0 7176 1604 5

7   *A guide to the Pipelines Safety Regulations 1996. Guidance on Regulations* L82 HSE Books 1996 ISBN 0 7176 1182 5

8   *Packaging, Labelling and Carriage of Radioactive Material by Rail Regulations 1996, as amended* SI 1996/2090 The Stationery Office 1996 ISBN 0 11 062921 3

9   *Railways (Safety Case) Regulations 2000 including 2001 amendments. Guidance on Regulations* L52 HSE Books 2001 ISBN 0 7176 2127 8

10   *Nuclear Installations Act 1965 Ch 57* The Stationery Office 1965 ISBN 0 10 850216 3

11   Home Office *Dealing with disaster* (Third Edition) Brodie Publishing 1997 ISBN 185 893 9208

12   Scottish Office (now Executive) *Dealing with disasters together* (Second edition 1998). (Available free from the Scottish Executive Emergency Planning Department Tel: 0131 244 2184)

13   *Safety representatives and safety committees* L87 (Third edition) HSE Books 1996 ISBN 0 7176 1220 1

14   *A guide to the Health and Safety (Consultation with Employees) Regulations 1996. Guidance on Regulations* L95 HSE Books 1996 ISBN 0 7176 1234 1

15   *Civil nuclear emergency planning. Consolidated guidance prepared by the Nuclear Emergency Planning Liaison Group* (NEPLG consolidated guidance). Available on the DTI website **www.dti.gov.uk/nid/neplg_guide.htm**

16   *Arrangements for responding to nuclear emergencies* HSE Books 1994 ISBN 0 7176 0828 X

17   *Management of health and safety at work. Management of Health and Safety at Work Regulations 1999. Approved Code of Practice and guidance* L21 (Second edition) HSE Books 2000 ISBN 0 7176 2488 9

18   *Atomic energy and radioactive substances: Radioactive Material (Road Transport) (Great Britain) Regulations 1996* SI 1996/1350 The Stationery Office 1996 ISBN 0 11 054742 X

19   *Documents of the NRPB*, Vol. 1 No. 4 1990 ISBN 0 85951 329 7

20   *Documents of the NRPB*, Vol. 8 No. 1 1997 ISBN 0 85951 407 2

21   *Review and assessment: Selection and use of dispersion models* LAQM.TG3(00) is available on the DEFRA website: **www.defra.gov.uk/environment/airquality/laqm/tg300/pdf/index.htm**

22   Reports from the Atmospheric Dispersion Modelling Liaison Committee (ADMLC) are available on the NRPB website: **www.nrpb.org.uk/projects/admlc/admlc-2.htm**

23   *A guide to the Dangerous Substances in Harbour Areas Regulations 1987* HSR27 HSE Books 1988 ISBN 0 11 883991 8

24   International Civil Aviation Organisation (ICAO) *The Technical Instructions for the safe transport of dangerous goods by air approved and published by decision of the Council of the International Civil Aviation Organisation* Doc 9284-AN/905 (Available from Freight Merchandising Services, Unit 19, Ashford Industrial Estate, Shield Road, Ashford, Middlesex TW15 1AU Tel: 01784 240840 Fax: 01784 248615 e-mail: info@fmslondon.co.uk or Labeline (Air, Sea & Road), Hollyhouse, 14 Tenby Road, Frimley, Surrey GU16 5UT Tel: 01252 836472 Fax: 01252 838094 e-mail: sales@labeline.com)

25   NRPB Research Report NRPB-M1311 *Calculations to assist in the revision of IRR-85 with respect to Special Hazard Assessments (REPPIR Schedule 2)* by A D Carey, K R Smith, C E McDonnell, S F Mobbs, P A Mansfield and W B Oatway, available from the NRPB Tel: 01235 831600

26   International Atomic Energy Agency *Regulations for the safe transport of radioactive material* TS-R-1 (revision of ST-1 1996) Vienna 2000 ISBN 9201005008

27   *Radioactive Substances Act 1993 Ch 12* The Stationery Office 1993 ISBN 0 10 541293 7

28   HM Railway Inspectorate Assessment Criteria can be viewed on **www.hse.gov.uk/railway/frameset/main.htm** (click 'show navigation'). See Section 4 (Risk assessments) and Section 11 (Emergency response arrangements)

29   *Carriage of Dangerous Goods by Rail Regulations 1996* SI 1996/2089 The Stationery Office 1996 ISBN 0 11 062919 1

30   Civil Aviation Publication CAP 168 *Licensing of aerodromes*, downloadable from the CAA website: **www.caa.co.uk**

31   RADSAFE - information available from the Operational Services Emergency Planning Group, British Energy, Barnett Way, Barnwood, Gloucester GL4 3RS

32   *Documents of the NRPB*, Vol. 5 No. 1 1994 ISBN 0 85951 371 8

33   *Transport of Dangerous Goods (Safety Advisers) Regulations 1999* The Stationery Office 1999 ISBN 0 11 080434 1

34   Home Office/Scottish Office Technical Bulletin 2/1993 *Incidents involving radioactive materials* The Stationery Office 1993 ISBN 0 11 341034 4

35   Council Regulation (Euratom) No. 3954/87 of 22 December 1987 laying down maximum permitted levels of radioactive contamination of foodstuffs and of feedingstuffs following a nuclear accident or any other case of radiological emergency *Official Journal of the European Communities* (1987) No L371, 11-13 amended by Council Regulation 2218/89 *Official Journal of the European Communities* (1989) **32**, No L211, 1-3

36   Commission Regulation (Euratom) No. 944/89 of 12 April 1989 laying down maximum permitted levels of radioactive contamination in minor foodstuffs following a nuclear accident or any other case of radiological emergency *Official Journal of the European Communities* (1989) **32**, No L101, 17-18

37   Commission Regulation (Euratom) No 770/90 of 29 March 1990 laying down maximum permitted levels of radioactive contamination of feedingstuffs following a nuclear accident or any other case of radiological emergency *Official Journal of the European Communities* (1990) No L833, 78-79

38   International Atomic Energy Agency's International Nuclear Event Scale (INES) can be viewed on **www.iaea.or.at/worldatom/inforesource/factsheets/ines.html**

39   Health and Safety Laboratory Research Report IR/L/FS/99/19 *Release fractions for radioactive sources in fires* by J T Allen, G Atkinson and A M Thyer, available from The Information Centre, Broad Lane, Sheffield S3 7HQ (A reproduction fee will be charged)

40   ISO 2919:1999 *Radiation protection – Sealed radioactive sources – General requirements and classification* International Standardization Organization

41   BS 5288:1976 *Specification. Sealed radioactive sources* British Standards Institution

While every effort has been made to ensure the accuracy of the references and web addresses listed in this publication, their future availability cannot be guaranteed.

British Standards are available from BSI Customer Services, 389 Chiswick High Road, London W4 4AL Tel: 020 8996 9001 Fax: 020 8996 7001 Website: **www.bsi-global.com**

The Stationery Office (formerly HMSO) publications are available from The Publications Centre, PO Box 276, London SW8 5DT Tel: 0870 600 5522 Fax: 0870 600 5533 Website: **www.clicktso.com** (They are also available from bookshops.)

Further reading

Home Office *Exercise Planners Guide* 1999 - available on the Home Office **website: www.homeoffice.gov.uk/epd**

Radiation protection off-site for emergency services in the event of a nuclear accident HSG63 HSE Books 1991 ISBN 0 11 885576 X

A guide to the Reporting of Injuries, Diseases and Dangerous Occurrences Regulations 1995 L73 (Second edition) HSE Books 1999 ISBN 0 7176 2431 5

Printed and published by the Health and Safety Executive